C000126639

Dragonfly

Dragonfly

DAVID CHANDLER AND STEVE CHAM

NEW HOLLAND

This edition published in 2013 by New Holland Publishers
London • Cape Town • Sydney • Auckland
www.newhollandpublishers.com

Garfield House, 86–88 Edgware Road, London W2 2EA, UK
Unit 1, 66 Gibbes Street, Chatswood, NSW 2067, Australia
Wembley Square, First Floor, Solan Road Gardens, Cape Town 8001, South Africa
218 Lake Road, Northcote, Auckland, New Zealand

Copyright © 2013 in text: David Chandler
Copyright © 2013 in photographs: 'Steve Cham, except other photographers as
credited below
Copyright © 2013 New Holland Publishers (UK) Ltd

10 9 8 7 6 5 4 3 2 1

All rights reserved. No part of this publication may be reproduced, stored in a retrieval system
or transmitted, in any form or by any means, electronic, mechanical, photocopying, recording
or otherwise, without the prior written permission of the publishers and copyright holders.

A CIP catalogue record for this book is available from the British Library.

ISBN 978 1 78009 229 4

Senior Editor: Sally McFall
Designer: Keisha Galbraith
Production: Olga Dementiev
Publisher: Simon Papps

Printed and bound in China by Toppan Leefung Printing Ltd

Photographs by **David Chandler** (pages 11, 20 [© Natural History Museum], 82–83, 119),
Norman Crowson (page 76), **Noah Elhardt** (page 78), **Flagstaffotos** (page 48 [bottom]),
Greg Lasley © Greg W. Lasley, www.greglasley.net (pages 12–13, 17, 29 [top right], 36, 41
[top], 42, 64, 74, 79, 85, 87, 91 [top], 99), **Deane Lewis**, http://dl.id.au (pages 2 – frontispiece,
29 [top left], 62), **Erland Refling Nielsen** (pages 15, 22, 34, 43, 46 [top], 49, 77 [bottom], 93
[bottom], 96, 128), **OpenCage** (page 33), **Reiner Richter** (pages 45, 59), **Warwick Tarboton**
(pages 9, 10, 19, 46 [bottom], 61, 86, 118, back cover), **Markus Varesvuo** (pages 66–67),
Roy Woodward (pages 26 [bottom], 27 [top and bottom], 41 [bottom], 55, 73, 80, 81, 90
[bottom], 92 [top], 111, 113).
All other photographs are by **Steve Cham**.

Front cover image: Banded Demoiselle *Calopteryx splendens* female. **Back cover image:** Yellow-
veined Widow *Palpopleura jucunda* female. **Front and end matter captions:** Frontispiece (Page
2) – The Painted Grasshawk *Neurothemis stigmatizans* can be seen in northern and northeastern
Australia. Page 128 – Red-veined Dropwing *Trithemis arteriosa* is a common African Dragonfly
also found in some parts of Turkey.

DEDICATION

This book is dedicated to Pat – a friend for decades.

ACKNOWLEDGEMENTS

First, a big thank you to Ruary Mackenzie Dodds, who knows more about Dragonflies than I do. Ruary suggested additional material to include, provided reference material and information on Dragonfly names in multiple languages, and was generous enough to read and comment on the text. Thanks Ruary – you made it better.

Henry Curry tipped me off about the beast of Bolsover; Charles Anderson, in the Maldives, helped with information on his research; Dr Ola Fincke at the University of Oklahoma corrected my Forest Giant text; and Steve Brooks, Theresa Howard, Suzanne Ryder and George Beccaloni at the Natural History Museum in London facilitated access to their impressive collection. Thank you all. Thanks also to Maureen Morris for providing some of the books that I used to research *Dragonfly* from Keith's, her late husband's, library; and to

Graeme King and Luke Paterson, in Australia, for their help.

Thank you to Simon Papps for commissioning me to write my fifth book for New Holland, and to Sally McFall for being so easy to work with, and for all that you did to improve my words. A book like this needs good photographs – thanks to Steve Cham, who provided about half of the photos, and to all the other photographers who put in the hours to capture the images that we have included. And thanks to Keisha Galbraith, the designer, for doing your bit to make this book look as attractive as it does. I also want to acknowledge the efforts of all of the scientists and enthusiasts whose work has provided the raw material for the words between these covers.

Finally, as ever, a big thanks to my family, for putting up with another book-writing project!

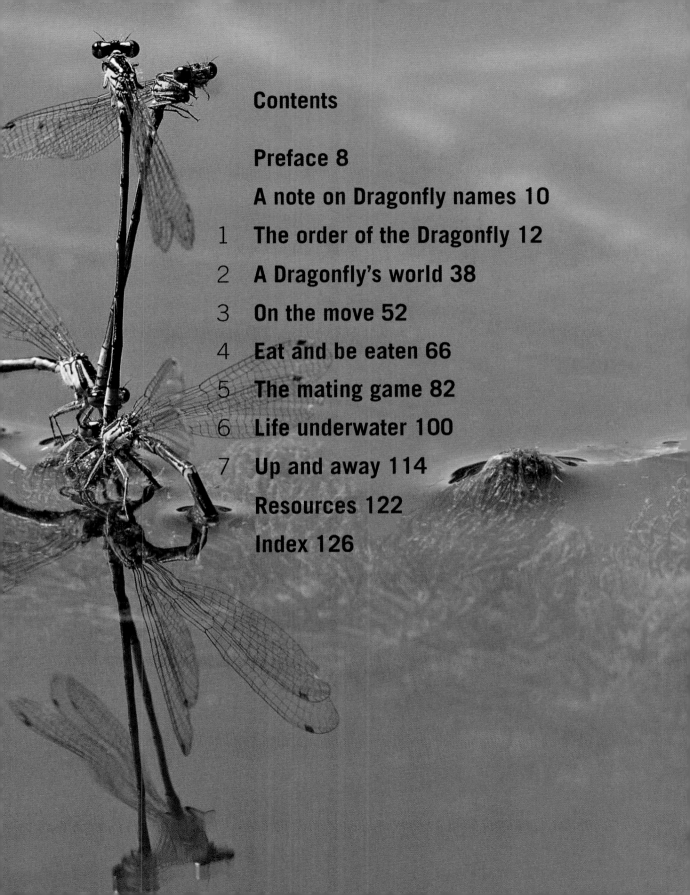

Contents

Preface

Like so many others, my interest in natural history started with birds. I write for *Bird Watching* magazine and I've also written books about birds. Here's a confession. These days, when the dragonflies are flying, they get me more excited than the birds. There's something about these masters of the air, these supreme predators, these blurs of colour, these floating, painted matchsticks, that has got well and truly under my skin.

My first attempts at identifying dragonflies date back about 30 years. I've been looking at them more seriously for about a decade, and I love it. I live in the UK, where the dragons are relatively well understood, but where there are still things to discover. There are not that many species in the UK, so they are a group that it is not too difficult to get to grips with. Other parts of the world have considerably more species and, therefore, greater identification challenges. But you don't need to know its name to appreciate a Dragonfly's beauty, flying skills and remarkable life cycle.

If you can work out which species you're looking at, you can make a genuine contribution to the biological record. One of my dragonfly-watching sites is a country park just outside Cambridge in England. I have a favourite spot here, where, standing in one place for about 90 minutes, I have identified nine different dragonfly species. That's not bad for a country with only around 45 species in total. I've added two species to the site's dragonfly list. That's not because I'm particularly good at it – it's more a reflection of the lack of observers.

Dragonfly is a book for anyone who wants to know more about Dragonflies. It is a book for those new to the joys of Dragonflies and for those who have been enjoying them for many years. My aim is to provide sound information in an accessible way. *Dragonfly* goes back to basics, but goes beyond basics, too. I hope that even the more knowledgeable Dragonfly enthusiast will find something that they didn't already know in the chapters that follow. Most of the photographs in this book are of species from Europe, North America, Australia and South Africa and many of its examples are drawn from these regions.

Pages 6–7: A group of Azure Damselflies *Coenagrion puella* egg-laying in tandem (you can read more about this in Chapter 5). The Azure Damselfly is a common European species.

Dragonfly begins with an overview of the world's damselflies and true dragonflies. The rest of the book includes information on how Dragonflies find their breeding sites, along with their flight, feeding, breeding and life cycle, from egg to larva to emergence and finally to glorious, airborne adult. You can read *Dragonfly* from start to finish, or just dip in. It is not the last word on Dragonflies – there is plenty more that could be said. But I hope it fuels your enthusiasm and whets your appetite for time in the field with these wonderful beasts.

Enjoy the book. Then, when the sun shines… you know what to do.

David Chandler

This beauty – a Yellow-veined Widow *Palpopleura jucunda* – can be seen in South Africa and other parts of Africa.

A note on Dragonfly names

'Dragonfly' is a label that can cause confusion. Sometimes it is used in the broadest sense to encompass true dragonflies and damselflies (see pages 30–31 for the differences), but at other times it refers only to true dragonflies. To avoid confusion in this book, Dragonfly, with a capital 'D', refers to the group as a whole – damselflies and true dragonflies. Where the text is referring only to true dragonflies those are the words that are used, never 'dragonfly' and never capitalized. Similarly, 'damselfly/damselflies' is never capitalized, unless it is part of a species' common name.

Not all Dragonflies have a common name, but when they do, I have used it. Note however, that some species have different common names in different parts of the world. All known Dragonflies have scientific names and these are used throughout, after the common name when there is one, to make it absolutely clear which species is being referred to.

Scientific names consist of two parts and are written in italics – *Anax imperator*, for example. The first part, *Anax*, is the genus. The second part, *imperator*, is the species. All species in the same genus are closely related, so *Anax junius* is clearly a close relative of *Anax imperator*, but a different species. Where it doesn't cause confusion, if two or more species from the same genus are mentioned, only the first species has the genus included in full. The others just have the initial letter of the genus, so *Anax junius* would be *A. junius*.

Below: The Red Groundling *Brachythemis lacustris* is a gregarious African true dragonfly species.

The author, with the beginnings of a Dragonfly pond in his garden.

About the author

David Chandler is a freelance writer and environmental educator. This is his fifth book for New Holland – he is the author of *Kingfisher* and *Barn Owl* in this series, and *All About Bugs* and *All About Garden Wildlife* for children. David is also a co-author of the *RSPB Children's Guide to Bird Watching* and *100 Birds to See in Your Lifetime*. He writes for *Bird Watching* magazine and *A Rocha*, the magazine of A Rocha UK.

David has a lifelong interest in wildlife and is a volunteer for the Dragonfly Project and the Dragonfly Centre at Wicken Fen in England.

About the photographer

Steve Cham has a long-standing interest in Dragonflies and has served as national co-ordinator for the Dragonfly Recording Network in the UK. He is the author of *Dragonflies of Bedfordshire* and the BDS *Field Guide to the larvae and exuviae of British Dragonflies*, co-author of *Dragonflies of Hampshire* and has written many papers on dragonfly behaviour and natural history. Steve was elected to honorary membership of the National Biodiversity Network Trust in 2008 in recognition for services to biological recording in the UK and awarded the Royal Entomological Society Marsh award for Insect conservation in 2011. Steve also serves on the Dragonfly Conservation group of the BDS.

1 | The order of the Dragonfly

N	o one knows how many different insect species there are in the
	world. So far, over a million have been named, and of these, around
6,000 are Dragonflies. Taxonomists divide the insect world into 26–29
orders of more closely related species. These include the Lepidoptera
(the butterflies and moths), the Coleoptera (the beetles) and the Odonata
(the Dragonflies). Odonata means 'toothed ones', a name that has its
roots in the powerful jaws of these awe-inspiring predators.

Where there be dragons

Apart from Antarctica, Dragonflies can be seen on every continent and
sometimes over the sea. In Europe and North America, their ranges
extend up to and beyond the Arctic Circle, reaching further north in
Europe than in North America, thanks mainly to the warming influence
of the Gulf Stream. There are Dragonfly records from Siberia at around
77°N, where the Azure Hawker *Aeshna caerulea*, the Subarctic Hawker
A. subarctica and the Northern Emerald *Somatochlora arctica* grace the
skies. To put that in context, the Arctic Circle is just over 66.5°N of the
equator. Some Dragonflies have extensive ranges and four species occur at
or beyond the Arctic Circle on both sides of the Atlantic – the Common
Hawker *A. juncea*, the Subarctic Hawker *A. subarctica*, the Treeline
Emerald *Somatochlora sahlbergi* and the Black Darter *Sympetrum danae*.

Dragonflies do not reach such extremes at the other end of the planet.
There are no records of any Dragonfly species south of the Antarctic
Circle. The most southerly record comes from Chile at a little over 55°S.
The identity of the Dragonfly in question is uncertain, but the most likely
candidate is *Rhionaeschna variegata*, a type of Hawker or Darner with no
common name.

But Dragonflies are at their most diverse and abundant in the
tropics, particularly where water flows through Latin American and
Asian rainforests. Indonesia is thought to have over 900 species. In stark
contrast, Europe has about 135 (the UK has about 45) and South Africa
has 158. With 324 species, Australia fares somewhat better, as does
North America with 433.

Pages 12–13: This is
Zenithoptera lanei, a very
striking South American
species. It is unusual among
true dragonflies in that it
sometimes rests with its
wings folded, rather than
sticking out to the sides.

Opposite right: The Subarctic
Hawker *Aeshna subarctica*
can be seen at or above the
Arctic Circle in Europe and
North America. The male
and female in this image are
mating. They are in the 'heart
position' or 'wheel position'
(see page 90).

Dragonfly Species Distribution

Region/country	Number of species
Australia	324
Czech Republic	72
Ecuador	300+
Europe	*c.*135
France	*c.*100
Germany	81
Indonesia	900+
The Netherlands	71
New Guinea and adjacent islands	*c.*430
North America	433
Solomon Islands	54
South Africa	159
Sri Lanka	116
United Kingdom	*c.*45

Water – the stuff of Dragonfly life

Almost without exception, Dragonflies need water to breed. They use a wide range of water bodies – the ones you would expect, such as ponds, lakes, ditches, streams, rivers, canals, bogs, swamps and marshes, and some more surprising ones.

Even a small amount of water can be enough for a Dragonfly to complete its life cycle. Their more remarkable breeding sites include the pools of water that gather where leaves meet their stems (in bromeliads, for example), in bamboo stems and in scrapes and hollows on trees. The Treehole Flatwing *Podopteryx selysi* is a big damselfly of the Australian rainforest. Its name tells you where it lives – pools in tree holes. The Roseate Skimmer *Orthemis ferruginea* of North and Central America normally breeds in more extensive patches of water, but sometimes takes advantage of pools in tree holes, too. There are species that

The Roseate Skimmer *Orthemis ferruginea* sometimes uses pools in tree holes for breeding. In this species, males occur in two colour forms – pink and red. This one is the pink form. The Florida Keys are a good place to look for the red form.

breed in birdbaths, puddles and even swimming pools! The group has
also conquered crashing waterfalls. The Giant Waterfall Damselfly
Thaumatoneura inopinata is at home amid the noise and spray of Costa
Rican and Panamanian waterfalls, and lays its eggs nearby. South Africa's
Scuffed Cascader *Zygonyx natalensis* is also at ease near waterfalls.

Islands and mountains

Even remote islands are home to Dragonflies. Five species live on the
Azores in the Atlantic; there are Dragonflies on the Chagos Archipelago
in the Indian Ocean and in Hawaii in the middle of the Pacific Ocean.
Some of the Hawaiian species have been introduced, but some are native.
The aptly named Globe Skimmer *Pantala flavescens*, which has a very
large global range, has been recorded on Easter Island in the South
Pacific and also holds the dragonfly altitude record. It has been seen
in the Nepalese Himalayas at 6,300m above sea level, though it is
highly likely that it was only there because air currents took it to
this lofty height.

Of more biological interest are the species that are known to breed
at high altitude. In Peru, the larvae of *Protollagma titicacae* (a damselfly),
or their shed skins, have been found at 4,720m above sea level. Those of
Aeshna peralta (a true dragonfly) have been found even higher at 5,050m
above sea level. This damselfly is a hairy insect, presumably to provide
some protection against low temperatures. Their existence at this altitude
is extreme, but not quite as extraordinary as it appears. These high-flyers
were living in a hot spring pond and hid in the grass near geothermally
heated soil when the sun went in!

Damsels and dragons

The Odonata order is divided into two suborders, the Anisoptera, which
means 'dissimilar wings', and the Zygoptera, which means 'similar wings'.
The 6,000 species are divided roughly equally between the two suborders.
To put things into more intelligible language, the Anisoptera are the true
dragonflies and the Zygoptera are the damselflies.

With just a little experience, telling the difference between the two is not difficult. The damselflies are more slender-bodied and when they take to the wing, they look like flying matchsticks. When they settle, with only a few exceptions, they hold their wings along their back. Their flight is fluttery and weak, and there is a gap between their eyes. Their front and back wings are a similar shape, but that can be hard to see in the field.

The true dragonflies have much stouter bodies and are strong fliers. When they settle, their wings are held open and stick out from the body, more or less at right angles to it. Most have eyes that touch (there are two families that don't). Their front and back wings are different shapes – this is easier to see because of the way they hold their wings when they perch.

The Scuffed Cascader *Zygonyx natalensis* is a species that can be seen near waterfalls. It is found throughout sub-Saharan Africa and is especially widespread in South Africa. It is also called the Blue Cascader or Powdered Cascader.

©Natural History Museum

In the classification hierarchy, 'family' is the next level of organization. The Odonata is made up of about 30 families, 60 per cent of which are damselflies.

Dwarves, midgets and giants

There are giants and midgets among these 30 or so families. *Megaloprepus caerulatus* is a stunning Latin American damselfly in the Forest Giant family. It takes spiders from their webs for food and has the biggest wingspan of any living Dragonfly. A specimen in London's Natural History Museum, collected in Costa Rica in 1988, has a wingspan of 19cm and a total body length of 12.1cm. Some Forest Giants are even longer – *Mecistogaster lucretia*, for example, is about 15cm long.

It is the true dragonflies that deliver when it comes to sheer bulk. There are several contenders, but the award for the biggest Dragonfly goes

This *Megaloprepus caerulatus* specimen is in the Natural History Museum in London. It was collected in Costa Rica. The male of this member of the Forest Giant family holds the record for the biggest wingspan of any living Dragonfly species. The coins shown in the image are a euro and a US dime.

to the Giant Petaltail *Petalura ingentissima*, a largely black species found by rainforest streams in Queensland, Australia. The females are bigger than the males and can have a wingspan of around 16cm and reach a length of 12.5cm. *Tetracanthagyna plagiata*, an Asian species, is another giant. A specimen of this species had its wingspan measured at 17.2cm!

There are a number of European species with a total body length of 80mm or more. The Bladetail *Lindenia tetraphylla*, several Goldenrings – including the Golden-ringed Dragonfly *Cordulegaster boltonii* – the Emperor *Anax imperator* and the Magnificent Emperor *A. immaculifrons* are all among Europe's giants.

Anax species are a recurring theme when it comes to big Dragonflies. The logically named Giant Darner *Anax walsinghami*, a species of California and the south-west United States, can reach a length of 11cm, and the Giant Hawaiian Darner *Anax strenuus*, one of Hawaii's endemics

The Emperor *Anax imperator* is one of Europe's biggest Dragonfly species – it can have a body length of up to 84mm. The one above is egg-laying. Compare its size to the accompanying Common Blue Damselfly *Enallagma cyathigerum*. Both are common European species.

(a species found nowhere else), is a similar size. South Africa's giant is the Black Emperor *Anax tristis* (see image on page 93), with a body length of about 12cm and a wingspan of around 13cm.

The midgets are found in a group known as... Midgets. Two species that are among the world's smallest are found in Australia – the Pinhead Wisp *Agriocnemis femina* and the Pygmy Wisp *A. pygmaea*. These tiny damselflies are just 1.6–1.8cm long. Among the true dragonflies there is a group known as the Dwarves, where perhaps, not surprisingly, the tiniest living true dragonfly is found. This is *Nannophyopsis clara* – a Chinese species with a wingspan of just 3.4cm.

Elsewhere, the Elfin Skimmer *Nannothemis bella* is North America's smallest true dragonfly (2cm long); the Dwarf Percher *Diplacodes pumila* is South Africa's (2.1–2.2cm long) and the Black Darter *Sympetrum danae*

The tiny Pygmy Wisp *Agriocnemis pygmaea*, shown here, is one of the world's smallest Dragonflies. This damselfly can be found in northern and eastern Australia and also occurs in central, west, south and south-east Asia. This is a male, recognizable by his orange-red tail-light.

(2.9–3.4cm long) is Europe's. The smallest damselfly in Europe is the Pygmy Damselfly *Nehalennia speciosa*, one of the Sedglings or Sprites, which is just 24–26mm long.

Typically, damselflies weigh 0.02–0.05g, which is next to nothing. True dragonflies generally tip the scales between 0.1g and 1g. That's not much either!

Digging up dragons

Dragonflies, or true dragonfly-like creatures, have been around for longer than almost any other group of flying insects. Some 325 million years ago there were insects in the air that looked much like the true dragonflies we see today. These ancient species were in an order called the Protodonata, or Griffenflies, a group that has no living representatives. Things were different in those days. There was more oxygen in the air than we are used to now, and these insects were much larger than the true dragonflies that we see today. It may have been the extra oxygen that made bigger bodies possible. The biggest species we know of was *Meganeuropsis permiana*, which is thought to have had a wingspan of 70–75cm. Imagine that. Imagine what those insects would have eaten. Imagine the size of their larvae. As far as we know, no larger insect has ever taken to the air. The ancestor of all living Dragonflies may well have been one of these ancient giants.

Fossils of 'modern' Dragonflies date back about 250 million years, and are very similar to today's species. Dragonflies from the Aeshnid, Gomphid and Petalurid families can be recognized in fossils that are 150–210 million years old, and broad-winged damselflies show up 65–150 million years ago. According to the fossil record, Libelluloid Dragonflies are relatively recent – they were not on the scene until 34–57 million years ago.

Coalmine dragonflies

The country most associated with fossil dragonflies is perhaps Germany, but it doesn't have the monopoly. In 1978, coalminers in Bolsover, Derbyshire, in England, made their contribution to the record. Malcolm Spencer was 586m beneath the surface when he found a fossilized 'dragonfly' wing. The size of the wing was such that the living creature would have had a wingspan of almost 50cm. It would have been flying over 300 million years before Malcolm started his shift. This species was new to science and was given the name *Erasipteron bolsoveri*, and then *Whalleyala bolsoveri*. Later that year, another miner was 600m below ground. He found another fossilized 'dragonfly'. This was named *Tupus diluculum*, which means 'Dragonfly of the Dawn', and then *Arctotypus diluculum*. Both species are Griffenflies from the Protodonata, rather than Dragonflies from the Odonata.

Dragonfly anatomy

Dragonflies are invertebrates with no internal skeleton. They wear their skeleton – an exoskeleton – on the outside. The exoskeleton is formed from toughened plates of chitin, with thin, flexible membranes between the plates. Chitin is a mix of polysaccharide and nitrogen. It is toughened with sclerotin, a protein-based compound.

Like all insects, a Dragonfly's body has three parts: the head, the thorax and the abdomen.

What's on the head?

- **Two, big, compound eyes:** As a proportion of body size, Dragonflies have the biggest eyes in the animal kingdom. Each eye is made up of a very large number of individual 'facets' or 'ommatidia'. A very patient Odonatologist (a scientist who studies Dragonflies) counted the facets on a Common Green Darner *Anax junius* eye – there were 28,672. Damselfly eyes do not have as many facets. Each facet has its own lens and forms its own image, which is one part of the whole view. Dragonfly eyes are very good at detecting movement. They can see forwards, sidewards, up and down and – by moving the head just a little – backwards, too.
- **Three simple eyes or ocelli:** These are on the top of the head and are thought to help with balance in flight.
- **Two small antennae:** Some species at least have 'sense organs' on

their antennae. These have been found to help the White-faced Darter *Leucorrhinia dubia* tell the difference between bog water and tap water. If you are in a part of the world where there are antlions, their more obvious antennae will help to avoid confusion with Dragonflies.

- **Mouthparts:** These are sharp, very powerful and open to the sides, not up and down.

This close-up of the eyes of a Southern Hawker *Aeshna cyanea* shows the many tiny facets or 'ommatadia' that make up a Dragonfly's eye. The three ocelli are arranged in a triangle between the two short antennae.

What's on and in the thorax?

- **Three pairs of legs, one on each segment of the thorax:** The lower surface of the thorax is tilted forwards, so the legs point forwards rather than down. No other insects are made this way. The spines on the legs lock together to form a catching basket, which you can find out more about on page 71.
- **Two pairs of wings, one on the middle and one on the rear segment:** more information about Dragonfly wings can be found on pages 54–57.
- **Huge flight muscles:** These form the powerhouse behind these master aeronauts.

What's on the abdomen?

- **Ten segments:** All Dragonflies have an abdomen with 10 segments. Dragonfly-watchers number them from 1 to 10, with number 1 being just behind the thorax, and number 10 at the tip of the abdomen. Segment 1 can be hard to see in the field.
- **Appendages:** These are at the tip of the abdomen. True dragonfly males have three – two above and one below. Male damselflies have four – two above and two below. True dragonfly and damselfly

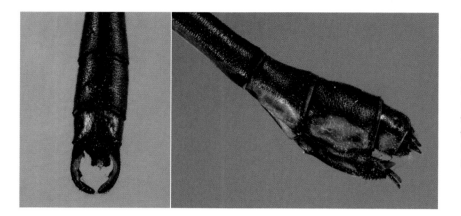

The appendages of the Willow Emerald *Lestes viridis*. Those of the male (far left) are used to grasp the thorax of the female. The female's ovipositor can be seen in the near left image, beneath the tip of her abdomen. This is used to insert eggs into plant material.

females have two. The males' appendages are used as claspers (see above left) to hold the female when 'in tandem' (see page 88–95) and when mating (see pages 84–93).

- **Genitalia:** Dragonflies do things differently to other insects. The male has two sets of genitalia, one under segment 9 and another –

In this close-up of a Black Darter *Sympetrum danae*, the secondary genetalia can be seen under segment 2 of the abdomen.

the secondary or accessory genitalia
– under segments 2 and 3. Sperm
has to be transferred from segment
9 to the secondary genitalia before
mating. The opening to the female's
vagina is under segment 8. Some
females have a well-developed
ovipositor for depositing eggs into
plant material or mud. Others have
reduced ovipositors and simply lay
their eggs on the water's surface
or nearby.

Male or female?

A good look at a Dragonfly's abdominal
appendages – and, if it's a male, its
secondary genitalia (a lump beneath
segment 2, seen on the opposite page
at bottom) – will help you work out its
gender. This isn't always easy though!

There may be colour differences
between males and females (the males are
normally more colourful), but this isn't
true of every species and an immature
male can be similar to a mature female.

Check the shape of the abdomen.
Typically, a female's abdomen is broader,
rounder and more parallel-sided, whereas
the male's may narrow towards the end or
be 'waisted' near the thorax (see the images above right).

There are some obvious behavioural clues, too. If you see two
Dragonflies in tandem, the male is the one in front. If you see two
mating, the male is the one holding on to the other one's head or thorax

The male Large Pincertail
Onychogomphus uncatus
(bottom) has a noticeably
thinner abdomen than the
female (top). Look at the
male's appendages – you can
see why species in this genus
are called Pincertails!

with its claspers – he's the one on top. If you see a Dragonfly egg-laying, it has to be a female!

Colour

The Dragonfly world includes beautiful, pigment-winged demoiselles, boldly marked red and blue damselflies, big black-and-yellow goldenrings, metallic green emeralds and bright red and powder-blue skimmers. Some of their colours are simply pigments. Some are structural colours, made by the way the exoskeleton reflects light. Some are the result of pruinescence – a powdery coating of pigment on the thorax and abdomen (see the top image on page 92), which covers the base colour with a layer of blue, white and rarely, red.

The males of some species use colour to make their presence obvious to the females that are potential partners, and to unwelcome males. The females of some damselfly species exist in different colour forms. Female Blue-tailed Damselflies *Ischnura elegans* (see image opposite), for example, have three colour forms. Intriguingly, where this occurs, in one of the colour forms the female looks like a male!

Colour can also be used to make a species hard to see – and hard to find – by would-be predators. Dragonflies use colour to control their body temperature, too. Those that are red, brown or black can warm up quickly, while paler colours could be a good adaptation to life at higher temperatures.

Their colours change as they mature, and more surprisingly, can change as the temperature rises and falls. This latter phenomenon has been observed in hawkers and six damselfly families and seems to be more common among Dragonflies than any other insects. Typically the species involved are red-brown or blue. They brighten when the temperature is higher than around 15°C, and revert to their duller colours, blue turning to grey, when it drops to less than about 10°C. The colour change can affect their eyes as well as their abdomens. It provides camouflage at lower temperatures when Dragonflies are less active, helps them to warm up when it's cool and stops them from getting too hot at higher temperatures.

The images on the right show a cornucopia of Dragonfly colour. Clockwise, from top left: the bold primary colours of Australia's Red Swampdragon *Agrionoptera insignis allogenes*; the bursts of black and white bands on the wings of North America's Twelve-spotted Skimmer *Libellula pulchella*; one of the colour forms of the female Blue-tailed Damselfly *Ischnura elegans*, with its pinkish thorax (a European species); and the iridescent blues and greens of Europe's Banded Demoiselle *Calopteryx splendens* (a male).

This male Azure Damselfly *Coenagrion puella*, with its blue-and-black markings, is a typical Pond Damselfly from the Coenagrionidae family and is one of Europe's most common species.

Some Families of Damselflies (Zygoptera)

Demoiselles (Calopterygidae)

These stunning damselflies have metallic bodies and broad wings that may be tinted or have very obvious and sometimes extensive patches of colour. Where there is one, there will often be plenty more.

Sylphs/Malachites (Synlestidae)

Sylphs are found in southern Africa, Australia, China and Hispaniola. They are big, metallic damselflies with stalked wings. In some species the wings are beautifully marked with black and white. Unusually for a damselfly, most perch with their wings held wide open.

Flatwings (Megapodagrionidae)

A diverse family of over 300 species, 22 of which can be found in Australia, flatwings live by streams in tropical rainforests. Typically, they are not brightly coloured and, like sylphs, break the rule and settle with their wings open.

Pond Damselflies (Coenagrionidae)

This very successful group of damselflies is typically small and thin, with stalked wings. Pond damselflies are easy to see. Many are blue with black markings. Most comply with the name and breed in still water.

Narrow-wings (Isostictidae)

The narrow-wings are well named. Their wings are very narrow and so are their bodies. These very delicate insects are not brightly coloured and are only found in Australasia. Australia itself has 15 species of narrow-wings.

Threadtails/Pinflies (Protoneuridae)

A diverse group of generally small damselflies with – as you might expect, given their name – very thin abdomens. Pinflies live in tropical forests, typically in areas with flowing water and some shade, and are very difficult to find. There may well be Pinfly species that have not yet been discovered lurking in a tropical forest somewhere.

Some Families of True Dragonflies (Anisoptera)

Hawkers (Aeshnidae)

The hawkers/darners are big true dragonflies that 'hawk' to and fro, searching for food. When they do finally settle, they normally hang vertically, often on a twig. These impressive creatures are found on every continent.

Clubtails (Gomphidae)

This is a very large family of ancient dragonflies, which are typically green or yellow with brown or black markings. Rivers and streams are their usual habitat. Unusually for a true dragonfly, there is a big gap between their eyes (this is also true of the petaltails*). Despite the name, there are clubtails that don't have clubbed tails!

Goldenrings/Spiketails (Cordulegastridae)

Either of these names provides a good description of these large, brown/black-and-yellow true dragonflies. The spiketail has a very long ovipositor that can reach way beyond the end of the abdomen. These striking creatures lay their eggs in flowing water, where the female pile-drives her ovipositor into sand or silt to make a hole for her eggs. Their eyes are blue or green.

Tigertails/Southern Emeralds (Synthemistidae)

Most tigertails are small or medium-sized true dragonflies. They have a thin abdomen and a hairy thorax. Typically, they are black or brown with yellow markings. Many are shiny. There are 26 tigertail species in Australia.

Emeralds (Corduliidae)

The norm for adults in this group is a metallic black or green insect with emerald green eyes. Some species are small. Some are large. Some have yellow markings. When an emerald settles, it hangs vertically. Emeralds have a global distribution but can be hard to find!

Chasers, Skimmers, Darters and Perchers (Libellulidae)

There are more species in this family than in any other true dragonfly family. Wherever there are Dragonflies, there are likely to be some of these. Some of these species have very extensive ranges. They are a highly variable group, and blue or red pruinosity is common. Typically, when they settle, they sit more or less horizontally, and fly out and back to the same perch.

*Petaltails are a small family of large true dragonflies. Their name comes from the male's petal-like appendages at the tip of the abdomen.

A Four-spotted Chaser *Libellula quadrimaculata*, one of the Libellulidae. Compare the broad body shape of this true dragonfly to the damselfly's matchstick-like body shown opposite. As a true dragonfly, it rests with its wings held out from the body – the damselfly has its wings folded along its back. Look at the eyes, too – here they touch each other; on the damselfly they are clearly separated.

Distribution of Some Dragonfly Families

Group	Family Name	UK	Europe	North America	South Africa	Australia	No. of species worldwide*
Damselflies							
Demoiselles	Calopterygidae	Yes	Yes	Yes	Yes	Yes	180
Sylphs/ Malachites	Synlestidae	No	No	No	Yes	Yes	35
Flatwings	Megapodagrionidae	No	No	?	No	Yes	313
Pond damselflies	Coenagrionidae	Yes	Yes	Yes	Yes	Yes	1,122
Narrow-wings	Isostictidae	No	No	No	No	Yes	45
Threadtails/ Pinflies	Protoneuridae	No	No	Yes	Yes	Yes	115
True Dragonflies							
Hawkers	Aeshnidae	Yes	Yes	Yes	Yes	Yes	445
Clubtails	Gomphidae	Yes	Yes	Yes	Yes	Yes	966
Goldenrings/ Spiketails	Cordulegastridae	Yes	Yes	Yes	No	No	52
Tigertails/ Southern Emeralds	Synthemistidae	No	No	No	No	Yes	154
Emeralds	Corduliidae	Yes	Yes	Yes	Yes	Yes	146
Chasers, Skimmers, Darters, Perchers	Libellulidae	Yes	Yes	Yes	Yes	Yes	993

* species totals from World list of Odonata, Martin Schorr and Dennis Paulson, 1 June 2012 revision

Epiophlebia

In the past, *Epiophlebia* species were placed with the damselflies in the Zygoptera, and on their own in a third suborder, the Anisozygoptera. They are now treated as a family within the true dragonflies in the Anisoptera but are a mix of typical true dragonfly and damselfly. Like true dragonflies, they have a stout body, are strong fliers and hang vertically when they settle. But when they are settled, they hold their wings like damselflies and, also like damselflies, their front and back wings are basically the same shape.

Until recently, only two *Epiophlebia* species were known to exist – the Japanese Relict Dragonfly *Epiophlebia superstes*, which lays its eggs in cold, fast-moving water in valleys in Japan, and the Relict Himalayan Dragonfly *E. laidlawi*, which lives in the

A specimen of the Japanese Relict Dragonfly *Epiophlebia superstes*

Nepalese Himalayas. In 2011, a third species, *E. sinensis*, found in China, was described. Then, in September 2012, Frank Louis Carle wrote about a fourth species, *E. diana*, in Arthropod Systematics and Phylogeny. This species is only known from two larvae that were referred to in *A Manual of the Dragonflies of China*, published in 1930! The larvae were found in western Szechuan in China and were misidentified as clubtail larvae. The larvae ended up at Cornell University and have now been re-identified.

Life cycle

There are many remarkable things about Dragonflies and one of them is their life cycle (this is covered in Chapters 5–7 in much greater detail). Most people are unaware that a very large part of a temperate Dragonfly's life is spent underwater as a larva. It's not unusual for this part of its existence to last for a year or two, and some spend much longer underwater. For a larva to grow it has to shed its skin, and it does this repeatedly. When it is ready to emerge, the larva climbs up a plant stem to get itself out of the water. The exoskeleton opens behind the head and the young adult hauls itself out of its last larval skin, which it leaves behind. This empty skin is known as an exuvia.

The immature adult heads away from the water to mature, and returns to water when it's ready to breed. Eggs are laid onto the water surface or into plant material or mud. They hatch into prolarvae, which quickly turn into larvae. Like the adults, the larvae are fierce predators.

In temperate regions, life as an adult Dragonfly is very short. If it survives emergence, a damselfly could live for one or two weeks, perhaps even four, and a true dragonfly for four to six weeks and maybe even eight.

Tropical and subtropical species adopt a different strategy. They may spend just a few months as a larva and a whole year as an adult.

Art, food, medicine and folklore

Traditionally, Dragonflies strike fear into Europeans, and hope into the Japanese and Chinese. In Europe, they have been given satanic connections, giving rise to names such as devil's needle, devil's horse and devil's spy. This is in stark contrast to Japan, where Dragonflies are associated with success, happiness, strength and bravery.

Dragonflies can be food items, too. A Balinese dish boils up Dragonfly larvae with shallots, garlic, chilli pepper and ginger in coconut milk, and true dragonfly adults are sometimes eaten as pudding in India. People in Japan, Indonesia, Thailand, Sumatra, Java, Mexico, China and Africa have eaten dragonflies, as larvae or as adults.

Chinese medicine has apparently prescribed true dragonflies, probably hawkers, as an alternative to viagra and to help with premature ejaculation – and damselflies to bring on ejaculation! And in Japan it seems that Scarlet Skimmer *Crocothemis servilia* may have been administered for syphilis, *Sympetrum darwinianum* for coughs and to help get fish bones out and *Orthetrum albistylum* for asthma.

But for most of us, it is the sheer beauty and wonder of Dragonflies that provides the connection. It is this that puts poets to work and spurs artists into action.

Opposite: These Black Darters *Sympetrum danae* have climbed up a plant stem as larvae to emerge as adults, leaving their last larval skin behind. The empty exoskeletons they emerge from are known as exuviae.

The Scarlet Skimmer
Crocothemis servilia is an
Asian species that was
accidentally introduced to
Florida in the USA. It was first
recorded there in 1975 and
has flourished in the south
of the state – this photograph
was taken in Fort Myers.

Local Names and Folk Names of Dragonflies

Country/area	Local/folk name, or translation of local/folk name
Arabia	The fan
Australia	Horse stinger
Bosnia	Snake's Tsar
Brittany, France	Air needle
Bulgaria	Water horse
Catalonia, Spain	Devil's spy
Croatia	Little fairy horse
England	Horse-adder, Adder-bolt
Finland	Wolf's water-pole
France	Devil's needle
Germany	Devil's horse
Greece	Eagle fighter
Holland	Water maid
Hungary	Colander
Ireland	Big needle
Italy	Eye stinger, Madonna's horse
Japan	Stick fly
New Zealand	Twinkle-water
Norway	Eye stinger, ear snail
Philippines	Fairy needle, fairy buffalo
Poland	Colander
Portugal	Devil's horse
Prussia	Gold-spinner
Russia	Whirler
Scotland	Bull snake
Slovenia	Snake's priest
South Africa	Needle case
Spain	Devil's horse
Sweden	Troll's spindle
United States	Hoss stinger, devil's darning needle, snake doctor, mosquito hawk, spinning Jenny
Wales	Snake's servant

2 | A Dragonfly's world

Most people associate Dragonflies with water, and particularly with the freshwater habitats that most species use as breeding sites.

What type of water?

Normally, Dragonfly water is freshwater. Some species, including the Blue-tailed Damselfly *Ischnura elegans* and the Migrant Hawker *Aeshna mixta*, both of which are European species, and in North America, the Big Bluet *Enallagma durum*, the Spotted Spreadwing *Lestes congener*, the Cherry-faced Meadowhawk *Sympetrum internum* and several other darters *Sympetrum* spp. can be found in brackish water. But there is only one species that lives in genuine seawater. This is the charmingly named Seaside Dragonlet *Erythrodiplax berenice*, a small skimmer that is found from northern South America to Canada.

Dragonflies breed in stagnant water and flowing water, but most do one or the other, and not both. Clubtails, for example, typically breed in flowing water, and pond damselflies in stagnant water. The divisions are not completely clear-cut – there are times when a flowing water species is found at the edge of a lake, where the waves turn otherwise still water into moving water.

Some Dragonfly species seem to be associated with acidic water – Australia's Dune Ringtail *Austrolestes minjerriba* and the Black Darter *Sympetrum danae* of Europe and North America, for example – but many species are not particularly picky when it comes to pH. Those that make a habit of breeding in acid waters seem to be species that can cope with a low pH rather than species that seek it out. It is thought that often it is not the pH itself that makes a site suitable or unsuitable for a particular species, but some other factor connected to the pH.

The Scarce Blue-tailed Damselfly *Ischnura pumilio*, a European species, can cope with quite a range of pH – it has been found in water with a pH of 8.1, which is very alkaline, and in water with a pH of 4, which is very acidic. The Four-spotted Chaser *Libellula quadrimaculata* and the Common Blue Damselfly *Enallagma cyathigerum* have been recorded in water with a pH as low as 3–4.

Pages 38–39: A swarm of Common Blue Damselflies *Enallagma cyathigerum* can contain hundreds of individuals, and is a great spectacle. This is a common European species.

Above opposite: This stunning creature is a Seaside Dragonlet *Erythrodiplax berenice*. The immatures have yellow stripes on the thorax and yellow or orange on top of the abdomen. They blacken with age, with the colour shift being quicker in males. Mature males are all blue/black, but not all mature females are. This species breeds in highly saline waters – estuaries and saltmarshes are good places to look for it.

Below opposite: A Black Darter *Sympetrum danae* covered in morning dew.

Good Dragonfly water is unpolluted. The Blue-tailed Damselfly *Ischnura elegans* seems to be particularly resilient to pollution, but most species are not. This means that, generally, Dragonflies are a good indicator of water quality.

Hot and cold water

Step into a hot tub and the water will probably be at a temperature of 37–39°C. That's only a little too hot for the larvae of Europe's White-faced Darter *Leucorrhinia dubia* to survive – they can cope to temperatures of around 35°C. But it would not be too warm for North America's Golden-winged Skimmer *Libellula auripennis*, which keeps going to 45°C. You wouldn't, of course, expect to see either species in a hot tub!

In Zimbabwe, temporary water pools can reach temperatures of over 36°C. Here, the Globe Skimmer *Pantala flavescens* and the Vagrant Emperor *Anax ephippiger* avoid the worst of the heat by loitering around the mud at the bottom, which can be about 10°C cooler than the water.

The larvae of most temperate species have to survive cold winters underwater. Exactly how they do this is not well understood, but those that face more extreme conditions may become inactive for a few months. Some larvae survive in waters that freeze over – either in the cold water underneath the ice, or even frozen in the ice itself – for four or five months. In Saskatchewan in Canada, larvae of the Taiga Bluet *Coenagrion*

You can almost feel the heat in this photograph of a Vivid Dancer *Argia vivida* – this species can survive in thermal springs.

resolutum and the Prairie Bluet *C. angulatum* spend the winter encased in snow-covered ice. The snow provides some insulation, and usually stops life in the ice from getting too cold!

There aren't many insects that live in thermal springs, but some Dragonflies do. The Vivid Dancer *Argia vivida*, a pond damselfly of the western United States, is one of them. It has two tricks up its sleeve to help it survive. Diapause, a period of arrested development, is one of them, and it can also adjust the number of generations it produces in a year. Together, these tricks enable this striking blue-and-black damselfly to emerge at an appropriate time and not be tricked by the higher temperatures.

Temporary water

A temporary pool of water would not appear to be the best place for a Dragonfly to lay its eggs. Yet when it happens, it doesn't always end in failure. Broad-bodied Chasers *Libellula depressa* and Blue-tailed Damselflies *Ischnura elegans* have emerged from puddles in wheel imprints. There are also species that lay their eggs somewhere dry in anticipation of it becoming wet. In Uganda, *Gynacantha africana* has been seen egg-laying in a dry scrape. A fortnight later there was water in the scrape, and larvae. The Red-tipped Swampdamsel *Leptobasis vacillans* lays eggs in dry scrapes in the Neotropics. A few days later, the rains come and the dry scrapes become wet pools. Exactly how these species know when and where to do this is unknown.

Red-tipped Swampdamsel *Leptobasis vacillans*, a damselfly that is one step ahead of the weather...

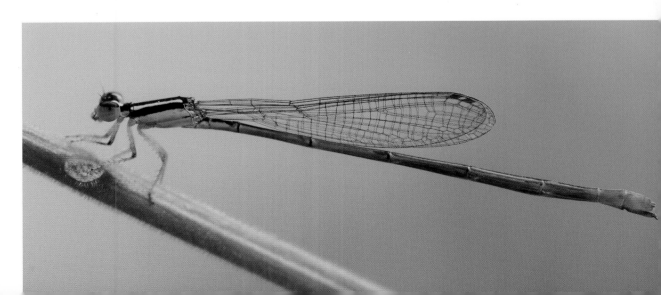

Not so aquatic

A small number of species have larvae that live in damp or wet places, rather than actually in water. One example is *Calicnemia miniata,* a damselfly of Nepalese forests. Its larvae can live on wet rocks amid moss, leaves and mud but away from pools or streams. A few species take things even further, including the Oahu Damselfly *Megalagrion oahuense.* The larvae of this Hawaiian endemic are found among fern roots and are completely terrestrial.

Sun-lovers and dusk-lovers

There are some Dragonfly species whose adults are associated with shadier conditions, but most are day-flying sun-lovers. The exceptions include the oft-mentioned Globe Skimmer *Pantala flavescens* – which can still be aloft in the rain as long as it's not too cool – and the Duskhawkers. The Duskhawkers and their relatives are crepuscular, which means that they are active around dusk and dawn, though they do sometimes keep more normal hours, especially when it's not too hot. These include South Africa's Little Duskhawker *Gynacantha manderica,* Australia's Cave Duskhawker *G. nourlangie* and North America's Twilight Darner *G. nervosa.* There are no Duskhawkers in Europe, but there are hawker species that fly late in the day.

Cooling down

Although mainly sun-lovers, there are times when Dragonflies need to take evasive action to avoid overheating. In broad terms, Dragonflies can be thought of as either fliers or perchers. Once a flier is up and about, it spends most of its time airborne. Typically, the larger true dragonflies are fliers – the hawkers are good examples. Small true dragonflies and damselflies tend to be perchers. As you might expect, these spend plenty of time settled, and only make short airborne sorties – to challenge an intruder or chase after a potential prey item, for example.

All dragonflies gain heat from the sun, but those that are fliers also make plenty of their own just by flying. Sometimes things get too warm. When a Dragonfly needs to lose heat, or avoid gaining it in the first place, it has a number of options. Simple solutions include finding somewhere cooler and avoiding activity during the hottest parts of the day. 'Obelisking' is another response. By pointing the tip of its abdomen at the sun, a Dragonfly reduces the surface area that the sun can warm directly, and this reduces the rate at which the insect heats up. There are species among the clubtails, the libellulids (chasers, skimmers, darters and perchers) and the demoiselles that adopt this posture (see images on page 46).

Australia's Southern Evening Darner *Telephlebia brevicauda* can be seen flying late in the day.

These stunning images are of Dragonflies 'obelisking' to avoid overheating. The image above is a Violet Dropwing *Trithemis annulata*. The lower image is a Barbet Percher *Diplacodes luminans*. Both are African species, but the Violet Dropwing can also be seen in parts of southern Europe.

Many libellulids have dark patches of pigment on their wings, especially at the base of the wings. This helps would-be mates sort one species out from another but could also help with temperature control by providing shade for the thorax. As mentioned on page 28, some Dragonflies change colour as the temperature changes. Hawkers often have coloured spots on the upper surface of their abdomen. In Azure Hawkers *Aeshna caerulea*, these spots change to more reflective colours at higher temperatures so that less heat is absorbed. This strategy may well be used by other hawkers, too.

Fliers may choose to glide more so that they generate less heat, and also lose heat by moving haemolymph (the nearest thing they have to blood) between the thorax and the abdomen. Dragonflies can also be seen dipping into water, and some will even immerse their whole body, which could help to keep them cool. They drink water, too.

Intriguingly, there are species, including some of the tropical dashers *Micrathyria* spp., that don't seem to do anything to control their temperature.

Warming up

Temperature control for Dragonflies is not just about avoiding overheating – there are plenty of occasions when Dragonflies need to raise their body temperature to be able to function effectively. An early morning emergence is one such occasion. When a Dragonfly emerges, it is in its own interest to be on the wing as soon as possible – while it is grounded it is easy pickings for a hungry predator. By vibrating its wings, a Dragonfly can generate its own heat and speed things along, enabling it to take to the air sooner than would otherwise be the case.

When they need to, Dragonflies will position themselves to soak up the sun and may use their wings as heat reflectors to help warm up the abdomen. Australia's Common Bluetail *Ischnura heterosticta* and Blue Ringtail *Austrolestes annulosus* are both known to 'sunbathe' when they are flying – the airborne insect lines up its abdomen to make the most of the morning sun.

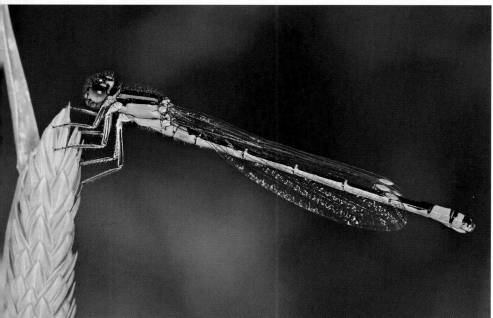

Above: Ruddy Darter
Sympetrum sanguineum is
a common European species.
This one is 'sunning' to warm
itself up.

Left: Common Bluetail
Ischnura heterosticta
is an Australian damselfly
that sunbathes in midair!

The importance of plants

Plants are an important part of most
Dragonflies' breeding sites. Some lay their
eggs into plants and their larvae may find
shelter among submerged plants, then
climb up emergent plants when the time
comes to leave the water behind. Plants
often serve as the actual site of emergence.
Adult Dragonflies use plants, too.
Damselflies settle on floating plants and
waterside vegetation, and 'perchers' base
themselves on sticks and stems from which
they make frequent aerial sorties.

Above: This Downy Emerald
Cordulia aenea larva is using
emergent plants to aid its
transition from aquatic larva
to aerial adult. This is a
European species.

Plants can be important away from
the breeding site, too. They are a vital
part of feeding habitats and places where immature Dragonflies can avoid
the hustle and bustle that is often a feature of breeding sites. Plants also
provide roosting sites for Dragonflies and shelter from inclement weather.

Most Dragonflies are not strongly associated with any one plant
species, though some do seem to be. The Green Hawker *Aeshna viridis*,
a species of north-east Europe, is a Water Soldier *Stratoites aloides*
specialist – the female lays her eggs into its leaves. She does use other
types of plant as well, but Water Soldier is the number one choice.

Having said all that, plants are not always an ingredient of a
Dragonfly breeding site and the species that normally use plant-free
sites sometimes leave their eggs in some surprising man-made 'pools' –
the Latin American *Libellula herculea* has laid its eggs in a can of water!

Finding a home

Every Dragonfly species has a preferred habitat or habitats. Some
are pickier than others. Becker's Pinfly *Roppaneura beckeri* must
surely be one of the pickiest. This damselfly lives in Brazil's Atlantic
rainforest and it seems that its larvae live in one place only – specifically,

the pools of water that collect where the leaves of *Eryngium floribundum*, an umbellifer, join its stem.

Most species are less critical and may even exploit different habitats in different areas. Some of the least picky are the pioneer species – the Dragonflies that seek out and take advantage of new breeding sites. These include Europe's Broad-bodied Chaser *Libellula depressa* and Blue-tailed Damselfly *Ischnura elegans*.

Yet however specific or generalized a Dragonfly's habitat requirements are, it has to find a suitable breeding site. For some, this is relatively straightforward, as they simply return to the site where they emerged. Europe's Southern Emerald damselfly *Lestes barbarus* adopts this strategy, but it seems that most species don't. After emerging, many fly some distance from their emergence site and must find a breeding site elsewhere.

Not surprisingly, when dragonflies are looking for a breeding site, water is the first thing most species look for. Dragonflies have UV receptors in their eyes. They are sensitive to polarized UV light and use the reflection polarization patterns created by water surfaces to find potential breeding sites. These patterns are influenced by the nature of the bottom substrate, how deep the water is and even by what is dissolved in it. As such, the patterns differ from one aquatic habitat to another, so they could be steering Dragonflies to the right kind of water body, and not just to any water body.

Dragonflies are visual insects and what they see plays an important part in the habitat selection process, from finding the right kind of water body to finding the right place to lay their eggs within or around that water body. What they see of the vegetation at a site helps them choose appropriately, and if they see other individuals of their species there – males displaying or females laying eggs – that's a good clue, too!

Other clues may come into play to help a Dragonfly work out exactly where to lay its eggs. This can include water temperature and the texture of what the eggs might be laid into. A female has sensory receptors on her ovipositor. Those species that lay their eggs into plants use these to help them choose exactly where the eggs will be deposited. Even the species

that lay their eggs on to the water's surface may check things out first with their ovipositor receptors – the Broad-bodied Chaser *Libellula depressa* might dip the tip of its abdomen to the water a number of times before it releases any eggs.

Above: A Broad-bodied Chaser *Libellula depressa* may 'test the water' before laying any eggs.

Sometimes a Dragonfly's use of reflection polarization patterns goes wrong. Some come to a sticky end in oil pools, river species mistake roads for waterways and some have tried to lay eggs on cars and other reflective surfaces. Common Darters *Sympetrum striolatum* have even been known to lay their eggs on ice.

There is still some Dragonfly behaviour that we do not understand. A Golden-ringed Dragonfly *Cordulegaster boltonii* flew along a stream for over 100m. Its route mirrored the route of the stream. The stream was underground with pavement on top of it. How did it do that?

The male Golden-ringed Dragonfly *Cordulegaster boltonii* is a handsome species that has demonstrated remarkable navigational abilities.

3 | On the move

No one can doubt the aerial prowess of adult Dragonflies, be it the jinking and sudden acceleration of a true dragonfly, or the gentler aerial agility of a damselfly. No insects fly better than Dragonflies. No other animals fly better than Dragonflies. And none of man's flying machines can match their abrupt changes of pace and direction, and their ability to fly forwards, backwards, sidewards, up and down, with glides and bouts of hovering thrown in to prove the point.

Pages 52–53: A Migrant Hawker *Aeshna mixta* male in flight.

Made to fly

Like butterflies and moths, Dragonflies have two pairs of wings. Unlike butterflies and moths, their front wings are not linked to their hind wings. This means that the two pairs of wings can move independently of each other.

For its size, a Dragonfly's wings are relatively large. They are also light and strong but not rigid. Their strength comes from a network of hollow veins. The vein at the front of the wing, the costa, is particularly substantial and provides strength along the leading edge. Behind this, the wing is more flexible but, unlike birds, Dragonflies cannot use muscles to control the shape of their wings. Research published in 2011 suggests that pads of resilin – a highly elastic protein – at vein junctions (where the veins that run along the wing meet those that cross it) provide a passive means of controlling this flexibility. In some species, tiny spikes on the veins at these junctions also play a part. Because the wing is flexible, it deforms in flight, but seems to do so in a way that helps rather than hinders flying.

The photo above right shows the 'node' and the 'pterostigma'. The node is rich in resilin. Not all Dragonflies have the node in exactly the same position. Beyond it, the wing can twist, and the nearer the node is to the thorax, the more the wing can twist. In hawkers, the node is roughly at the midpoint of the wing. In the libellulids, it is nearer the wingtip. In many damselflies it is just over a third of the way out from the thorax. The node can also function as a shock absorber.

The pterostigmata (which literally means 'wing marks'; pterostigma is the singular) add weight, help to control inertia and can enable a

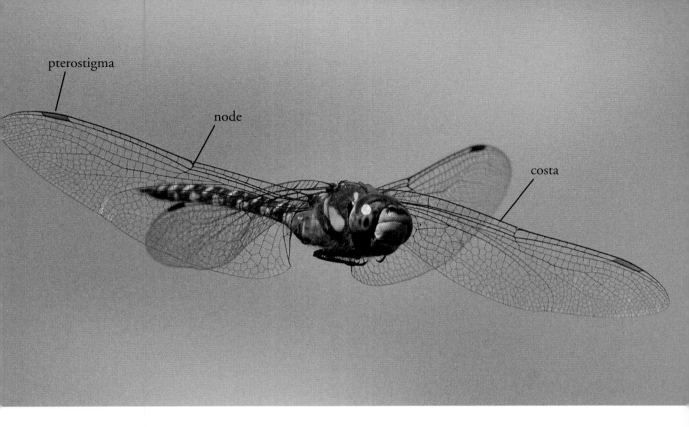

pterostigma

node

costa

Dragonfly to glide as much as 25 per cent faster than would otherwise be possible.

Aviation fuel

Dragonflies are fuel-efficient flying machines, but they still need lots of fuel and lots of oxygen. Their fuel comes in the form of fats or carbohydrates. Fats are the fuel of choice for longer journeys and, prior to migration, a Dragonfly may build up substantial fat reserves.

The oxygen comes in through holes called spiracles and reaches the muscles via tubes called tracheae. The beating of the wings changes the volume of the thorax and, as a consequence, it works like a pump, delivering plenty of oxygen to the massive flight muscles. A true dragonfly's flight muscles account for about 25 per cent or more of its weight, while those of a damselfly make up about 17 per cent of its total weight.

The mechanics of flight

Because a Dragonfly's front wings are not coupled to its hind wings, the four wings can beat in synchrony, or one pair can lag behind the other.

This excellent photo of an airborne male Migrant Hawker *Aeshna mixta* shows the pterostigma, node and costa. The main text tells you more about the function of these parts on a dragonfly's wing. The Migrant Hawker is a small European Hawker.

Damselflies are so light that even moving through the air is a challenge. Typically, a damselfly beats its wings about 35 times a second. It beats its wings asynchronously – when one pair is going down, the other is going up – in a movement called 'counterstroking'. When the wings are moving downwards they produce thrust, which moves the insect forward. In counterstroking, there is always one pair of wings moving downwards so the hard-working damselfly is always producing thrust. Counterstroking is fuel-efficient locomotion. Among the damselflies, demoiselles are the exception – they do not employ counterstroking. As a rule, you will not see a damselfly gliding or soaring unless you are in the company of Forest Giants (Pseudostigmatidae) in a Latin American rainforest. These are very large damselflies and it is their size that makes gliding viable.

Whereas the front and hind wings of a damselfly are narrow at the base and similar in shape (see below), those of a true dragonfly are not. A true dragonfly's wings are broader near the body and can function as aerofoils. This, along with the true dragonfly's greater size, equips these creatures for gliding and soaring. When a true dragonfly flies forward, its wings beat out of synch, but unlike damselflies, they are not counterstroking. The norm is for a true dragonfly's forewings to beat about a quarter of a wingbeat behind the hind wings. This technique moves the insect forward faster than counterstroking would.

True dragonflies use counterstroking to hover (see image above opposite). Hovering is energetically very demanding. The hovering insect must generate opposing forces that cancel each other out so that the creature stays in one place. When a hawker hovers, it beats its wings about 30° off vertical; when a damselfly hovers, its wings beat almost horizontally.

Sometimes the two pairs of wings do beat in synch, a technique that gets through a lot of 'fuel', but one that is commonly adopted by

'Counterstroking' is the normal flight mode for most damselflies. When one pair of wings is going down, the other is going up, as shown by this Red-eyed Damselfly *Erythromma najas*.

the demoiselles. True dragonflies use synchronized wingbeats to dart up vertically, or to shoot back and up.

But none of this explains the sudden changes of direction that Dragonflies are capable of. 'Banking' in midair is one way of turning a corner, but it cannot produce the sharp, jinking turns that bring predator to prey, and pleasure to the observer. A Dragonfly's design makes asymmetric wing actions possible, with the wings on the left doing different things to the wings on the right. In fact, all four wings can move independently of each other. This makes for complex aerodynamics. When a Dragonfly produces more speed on one side of its body than the other, it turns a corner. Gently moving damselflies are particularly adept at sharp turns – spend some time watching them move among pond-side vegetation to see what they are capable of. Their wing joints help them to do this, as they allow the wings to beat in any plane from horizontally right through to vertically. In a true dragonfly, the wing joints are much less versatile – all they can do is move their wings up and down.

Brilliant Emerald *Somatochlora metallica* hovering. The 'waisted' abdomen tells us that this is a male.

Winging It – Dragonfly Facts and Figures

- A damselfly can turn through 180° with just one wingbeat!
- The wingbeat frequency of the Emperor *Anax imperator* has been measured at 31 beats per second. That's 1,860 beats a minute. Among the libellulids, 30-40 wingbeats per second is not unusual.
- When they are beating fast, the tips of a true dragonfly's wings can move at about 25kmph (15mph). Those of a damselfly can hit around 9kmph (6mph).
- A true dragonfly can fly at speeds of 40kmph (25 mph), but only briefly. A flight speed of about 3.6–11kmph (2–7mph) is typical for a smaller damselfly. A speed of 85kmph (53mph) has been claimed for the Common Green Darner *Anax junius*.
- Hawkers can stay aloft for several hours. *Tramea virginia*, an Asian saddlebag glider, can stay airborne for over five hours.
- Some Dragonflies fly along in tandem (the male holding on to and pulling the female) for over 20km (12 miles).
- The large wings and relatively low weight of Dragonflies means they can still fly when their wings are badly damaged. Some fly when only one pair of wings remains. Research published in 2010, however, showed that wing damage does reduce a Dragonfly's flying abilities.

A male Emperor *Anax imperator* in flight. It can beat its wings over 30 times a second.

First flights

One of the most vulnerable parts of a Dragonfly's life is the period immediately after emergence – when the young adult has left its larval life behind but is not yet able to fly. Once it takes to the wing, the newly airborne insect is preprogrammed to fly away from water. Maiden flights vary in length. Those of the Tule Bluet *Enallagma carunculatum* and the Boreal Bluet *E. boreale* (North American damselflies) have been measured at an unimpressive 53cm and 42cm respectively. Some maiden flights are much longer and a greater distance may be covered after an initial short hop. Work by Norman Moore back in the 1950s found that an average maiden flight for the Four-spotted Chaser *Libellula quadrimaculata* was around 20m. Some maiden flights take the novice pilots hundreds of metres from their larval home. Moore's work recorded Emperors *Anax imperator* flying well over 200m on their maiden flight.

A very long maiden flight

Low-level flying is hard work, but greater distances can be covered with minimal effort by gaining altitude and letting wind currents do the work. The Aurora Bluetail *Ischnura aurora* is a very small damselfly whose extensive range includes the whole of Australia. When female Aurora Bluetails emerge, the males are already waiting and mating can occur before or during the maiden flight. In this species, they are not maidens for long! When they have mated, the females ascend and are whisked away by wind currents. The eggs are laid four or five days later at sites that can be hundreds of kilometres from the egg-laying adults' emergence site. Aurora Bluetails turn up at water in the middle of the desert and even find their way to oceanic islands after being carried over the sea by air currents.

Aurora Bluetails *Ischnura aurora* in tandem – this mature male is holding an immature female.

Water shy

The strategy adopted by most Dragonflies when they are new to their aerial existence is to keep well away from water. Having embarked on its maiden flight, an Emperor *Anax imperator* will avoid other water bodies. This aversion to water is likely to be common in most immature Dragonflies. It can take anywhere from a few days to over two weeks for a Dragonfly to mature, at which point it has to return to water to complete its life cycle.

Short visits

Work in Germany by Jochen Lempert found that at just one pond, many, many Dragonflies were arriving and departing – 27 different species flew in and over 1,600 darters found their way to the study pond in one year. Most of the incoming Dragonflies were mature individuals, but few of them were there for long – only one in 50 were present four to seven days after finding the pond. This suggests that it is normal for large numbers of Dragonflies to be on the move, actively seeking a suitable breeding site.

Once a Dragonfly has found a suitable breeding site, it is not likely to move that far from it. In a British study by Allen and Thompson published in 2010, over 2,000 Southern Damselflies *Coenagrion mercuriale* were marked. This species is not a great traveller – it is thought to be the UK's most sedentary Dragonfly species. The average distance moved in its lifetime was just 56m.

On a daily basis, a Dragonfly will move between its roost and the place where it feeds and seeks to breed. These can be just metres apart or a few kilometres. As a rule, Dragonflies are not great travellers. Most don't travel very far, but there are some notable exceptions.

Longer journeys – taking refuge

Some Dragonfly species take part in 'seasonal refuge flights'. Immatures will leave their emergence site and take refuge for a season somewhere else. This can be as close as 100m to the larval home or many kilometres away. They leave as immatures and are in diapause (a period when development stops) for a season before they return to breed.

Migrant Hawkers *Aeshna mixta* in Algeria emerge from lowland ponds but spend the summer, when the ponds dry out, in the uplands. Their transition to sexually mature individuals is triggered by rainfall. They then fly back to the lowland ponds, which now have water in them and are suitable for egg laying. Some darter species in North Africa and elsewhere also take 'seasonal refuge'.

Wandering vagabond – the Vagrant Emperor

The Vagrant Emperor *Anax ephippiger* breeds in Africa, the Middle East and parts of Asia, often in temporary pools, where the larvae can become adults in just two or three months. It is a well-named species, a creature that moves with weather fronts that bring it in just ahead of the rain. After a good breeding season, large numbers of Vagrant Emperors can be on the move. Its travels bring it into southern Europe, and sometimes further north. It has turned up in the UK on a number of occasions, with a particularly memorable record from Cornwall on 16 April, 2011, when Kevin Wilkes' wife found a Vagrant Emperor on the washing! That year brought the biggest influx of Vagrant Emperors in to the UK to date. A major movement was taking place – there were thousands in Israel and the UAE, and big numbers in Spain and flying north in Portugal. Historically, the Vagrant Emperor has been recorded as far north as Iceland and, after a trans-Atlantic journey, as far west as the Caribbean.

The Vagrant Emperor *Anax ephippiger* – no other Dragonfly species is known to have made it to Iceland.

On 7 September, 1990, I was in the Camargue in the south of France. I was interested in Dragonflies but my knowledge was limited. Here's an extract from my notebook:

> *'Driving home at dusk was an experience – hundreds of large dragonflies were hunting along the road, and driving through them was a bit like a scene from* Star Wars*!'*

I now know that millions of Vagrant Emperors arrived in France and Italy that year.

A truly remarkable story – the Globe Skimmer

The Globe Skimmer *Pantala flavescens* is probably the Dragonfly world's best-known traveller. It has an extensive range that includes tropical areas and most of the United States and Australia. It lays its eggs in temporary pools. To survive, the larvae must grow quickly, becoming adults in about six weeks. The adults move with the weather, arriving just ahead of the rain that makes the pools they need to lay their eggs in.

Charles Anderson is a marine biologist working in the Maldives, a chain of islands in the Indian Ocean. His curiosity was aroused by the annual arrival of millions of Globe Skimmers. Some of the evidence is circumstantial, but the story he has pieced together is convincing. The Globe Skimmers arrive on the Maldives from India to the east, having crossed 600–1,000km (375–625 miles) of sea. The prevailing winds at this time are from the west, so it appeared that the insects were flying into the wind. Actually, they make their sea crossing at high altitude,

Globe Skimmer *Pantala flavescens* is unique among insects – it is a regular trans-oceanic migrant.

1,000–2,000m or more above sea level, and at this altitude they have a tail wind. There is virtually no freshwater on the Maldives, which means that there is nowhere for the newly arrived Dragonflies to breed. Crossing to the Maldives is thought to be just one part of a migratory jigsaw, a stop-off during a bigger journey in which the wind takes these remarkable creatures from breeding site to breeding site. As the rains move, the Dragonflies move. It seems that Globe Skimmers fly a circuit of the Indian Ocean, from India to East Africa and back to India. It is a circuit that totals 14,000–18,000km (8,750–11,250 miles). No other insect is known to cross oceans on a regular basis. But there is no one individual Skimmer that completes the circuit – it takes four generations to do that.

A paper published in 2012 shows that this story is even more remarkable. By analysing the isotopes in a Dragonfly's wing, it is possible to determine the region that the individual came from. This work proved that the Globe Skimmers that reach the Maldives originate not from the south of India but from the north of India, and possibly even further north.

Touring America – the Common Green Darner

This species' range includes Central and North America, and reaches into the southern parts of Canada. In Florida, adults emerge throughout the year. Further north, the Common Green Darner *Anax junius* can be a resident species and a migrant.

In some parts of Canada and the USA, these bulky darners are on the wing before any Dragonflies have emerged locally. The airborne individuals are not local stock – they are migrants that emerged further south and flew north. It is perfectly possible to see this species in the air while there is still snow on the ground and even ice on the water. Generally, the females have already mated when they arrive and are soon laying eggs. Larval development is rapid and the migrants' offspring emerge from the end of July to October. These immature adults carry plenty of fat. They stay a while, perhaps weeks, and then fly south, burning fat to fuel the journey to their southern breeding sites. It is a round-trip migration, but like the Globe Skimmer, it takes more than

one generation to complete the trip. When they fly south they usually do it en masse, along with many other Common Green Darners. They may also be accompanied by migrating hummingbirds, hawks and Monarch butterflies *Danaus plexippus.*

Mass movements

Some Dragonfly journeys are less predictable. The Four-spotted Chaser *Libellula quadrimaculata* is one example. In Europe especially, this species migrates in spring in swarms, but not every year – on average about once a decade. In 1971, huge numbers were on the move in Belgium and the Netherlands. Like European Starlings *Sturnus vulgaris* massing on their way to a roost site, one group joined another, and then another, to form huge swarms, some of which were 6km (3.75 miles) long. But within a few days, the insects seemed to have burnt themselves out – they were crashing into things and were easily caught by cats and birds.

Staying in Europe, the Migrant Hawker *Aeshna mixta* and a variety of darter species (*Sympetrum*) sometimes indulge in mass movements.

Some Common Green Darners *Anax junius* are migrants. One generation flies north, and their offspring fly south.

Numbers of Dragonflies in the UK are supplemented by Migrant Hawkers and darters that find their way across the sea from mainland Europe, either regularly or sporadically. When Yellow-winged Darters *Sympetrum flaveolum* arrive in force, which happens occasionally, it can be spectacular!

How do Dragonflies find their way?

Dragonflies are highly visual creatures and sometimes navigate simply by following the course of a road, railway or waterway. Some migrating Dragonflies fly along coastlines, though this could, at least in part, simply be the result of not wanting to be on the wing over the sea. Migrating Dragonflies are also thought to use the Sun as a compass, which might help to explain how some can hold a steady course that ignores linear features on the ground and stays constant even when the wind changes direction.

How to track a Dragonfly

Radar can detect true dragonflies that are on the move at high altitude, but it is only recently that technology has allowed the tracking of individuals.

In 2005, a team led by Martin Wikelski in the USA glued radio transmitters under the thoraxes of 14 Common Green Darners *Anax junius*. The transmitters weighed about 0.3g. The signals could be picked up from about 1.6km (1 mile) away on the ground, and from about 8km (5 miles) away from a light aircraft. The team found that the Darners journey south was not non-stop, that they stayed put if it was too windy and didn't travel at night. They continued their journey on every third day (more or less), and covered an average of 58km (36.25 miles) over about six days. When they were migrating, they sometimes flew over 100km (62.5 miles) in just one day. They only moved on if the nocturnal temperature dropped on two consecutive nights.

Radio tracking has also been used to study movements and home range size at a local level. In 2010, Sarah Levett and Sean Walls used superglue and eyelash adhesive to fix radio tags on to five Emperors *Anax imperator*. There were no firm conclusions, but who knows what may be possible as technology develops further.

4 | Eat and be eaten

Dragonflies are voracious predators as larvae and as adults. This chapter looks at adult Dragonflies, both as predators and as prey (Dragonfly larvae as predators and prey is discussed in Chapter 6).

Pages 66–67: When predator becomes prey – some bee-eaters take Dragonflies as well as bees.

The anatomy of a killer

A Dragonfly's design makes it well suited to a predatory lifestyle. Its huge compound eyes are quick to pick up movement, even at a distance. They can see to the front and sides, above and below, and with a small turn of the head, behind as well. They can probably see in colour, and some at least have eyes that function well in low light – there are some Dragonflies that hunt at dusk.

Some parts of their eyes see better than others. If you take a good look at a Dragonfly's eye, you should be able to see an upper and a lower region. Typically, the facets or ommatidia are smaller in the lower region. Each region has 'acute zones' – areas that produce particularly sharp images. Acute zones have larger ommatidia or facets. The more parallel the ommatidia are, the better the resolution.

Get close to a damselfly and look into its eyes. Look for big black 'pseudopupils' – these are acute zones. Small pseudopupils are good at seeing movement but are not high-resolution areas. Watch one of the perchers. You may see small head movements – this is 'head cocking' and could be the Dragonfly getting a better view of something by moving it into an acute zone. When a Dragonfly grabs its prey in midair, it normally attacks from underneath. Dragonfly eyes are particularly good at spotting movement above them – by striking from below, this hunter-par-excellence can get the image of its prey into an acute zone before going in for the kill.

The upper and lower regions of the compound eyes are easy to see on this Four-spotted Chaser *Libellula quadrimaculata*.

The compound eyes of many libellulids are very clearly divided into upper and lower regions. There is an acute zone at the front of the upper eye – an arrangement that works well when hunting from a perch. Compare that to the compound eye of a hawker. The acute zone of these fliers is a thin strip that goes across the eye and equips them well for spotting prey during flight. It gets better. The acute zone can pick out prey against the sky. In hawkers that hunt in deserts, the acute zone is positioned lower on the eye than it is on those that hunt in coniferous forests where the horizon is higher. To make it easier to spot prey, the way a Dragonfly sees UV and blue light enhances the apparent brightness of the sky, so their next meal becomes more conspicuous. Dragonfly eyes gather a lot of information and considerable processing power is needed to make sense of it all. That may be the job of over 80 per cent of a Dragonfly's brain.

The structure of a Dragonfly's wings and its powers of flight are other key components of their killer anatomy. These were explored in Chapter 3, but no mention was made of their 'head arrester system' – something that is found only in Dragonflies. The head arrester system consists of very small 'hairs' on the neck and on the back of the head. These enable the head to hold its position during flight – it doesn't have to twist when the thorax does. This allows for a steady view and provides protection from sudden movements.

The three ocelli on the top of the head help to keep the Dragonfly level in flight. They are light-sensitive and arranged in a triangle, with the point facing forwards. If the ocellus at the front detects less light, the insect is dipping down and can quickly correct its course. The rear ocelli to the left and right work in a similar way in order to correct rolling, but all of these signals can be ignored when desired.

Dragonflies see well and fly well, but to hunt successfully they need a catching method too. As was previously explained in Chapter 1, Dragonflies are

Look at the position of the head of this Migrant Hawker *Aeshna mixta* relative to the rest of its body. The 'head arrester' system makes it possible to keep the head level when the thorax twists.

unique among insects in that their legs point forwards rather than down. As a consequence of this design, adult Dragonflies cannot walk. Their legs are used as a hunting (and perching) tool rather than for locomotion. The spines on the legs interlock to form a catching basket. This is one way they catch their prey, but it is not the only way.

Opposite page: The legs of this Banded Demoiselle *Calopteryx splendens* show the spines that are used to form its 'catching basket'.

Grabbing a meal

Dragonflies catch their prey in midair or by 'gleaning'. The midair hunters are essentially either fliers that grab their prey, and often eat it, during long periods in flight, or perchers that dart out from a perch after prey and return to a perch to eat it. In cooler conditions, a percher can struggle to maintain its body temperature and may behave more like a flier. In contrast, gleaning involves catching prey that is more or less static, by taking it off a plant, for example.

The fliers include the hawkers (Aeshnidae), the cruisers (Macromiidae), the goldenrings (Cordulegastridae), the tigertails (Synthemistidae) and the emeralds (Corduliidae). The perchers include most damselflies, the clubtails (Gomphidae), the petaltails (Petaluridae) and, of course, the majority of the chasers, skimmers, darters and perchers (Libellulidae). Many damselflies are both perchers and gleaners. Mostly, feeding does not occur at the breeding site.

Dragonflies do use their basket of legs to catch their prey, but not always. We know, for example, that some hawkers and some Emerald damselflies catch small insects with their mouthparts. They may not always do this – and they may use their catching basket to take more substantial prey items or to bring an uncooperative meal under control – but sometimes at least the food goes straight to the mouth. If the victim isn't too big, it may well be eaten on the wing. A bigger catch is normally eaten after its wings have been removed, and the Dragonfly may land before eating it.

The gleaners hover, dash and grab. The hunter hovers near its prey, then darts to it and uses its legs to grab its meal. The Forest Giants of Latin America are gleaners and spider-catching specialists. When the spider has been pulled off its web, this large damselfly goes into reverse, taking care not to get trapped in the web. Forest Giants are not the only damselflies that take spiders. The Blue-tailed Damselfly *Ischnura elegans*, a common European species, also takes spiders from time to time, as do other *Ischnura* species.

Eating habits

Dragonflies don't always eat alone. It is not unusual to see a feeding swarm of hawkers feasting on flying ants, or grabbing prey blown off trees by the wind. Groups of Globe Skimmers *Pantala flavescens* and Spot-winged Gliders *P. hymenaea* sometimes plunder the insects disturbed by animals or people.

Europe's Dusk Hawker *Boyeria irene* is one of a handful of species that feed at the end of the day. Like its supper, which is there in abundance, the Dusk Hawker comes to lights.

It is not the norm for Dragonflies, but some species feed in the rain. The Forest Darner *Austroaeschna pulchra*, which is found in Australia, is one example. It is hard to see a Forest Darner when the sun is shining, but when it rains it is out and about searching for prey around the tree canopy.

Demoiselles *Calopteryx* use a cunning catching method. They make a mesh with their legs and hold their coloured wings to block the view, making escape less likely.

What do Dragonflies eat?

Dragonflies take a wide range of insects, especially flies, with midges and mosquitoes as particular favourites. The box on page 74 gives an idea of the diversity of insects, other than true flies, that are eaten by Dragonflies.

Almost without exception, and as the list suggests,

Opposite right: An Azure Damselfly as prey – this one has been taken by a Blue-tailed Damselfly Ischnura elegans.

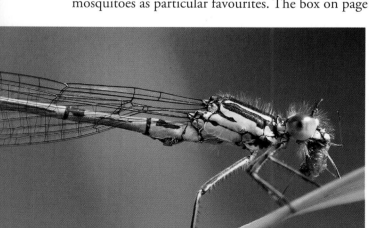

Left: An Azure Damselfly Coenagrion puella as predator – this one is eating an aphid.

Dragonflies are opportunist predators. It is not particularly unusual for a Dragonfly to take a butterfly (see the image right). Even large butterflies can be captured – the Dragonhunter *Hagenius brevistylus*, a large clubtail found in North America, has been known to take a Monarch *Danaus plexippus*. Caterpillars dangling on threads are taken, too.

There is no clan loyalty either. A true dragonfly may well eat a damselfly or even another true dragonfly. The Emperor *Anax imperator*, a large European hawker, has been recorded eating a male Common Darter *Sympetrum striolatum*, a much smaller species, that was in tandem at the time. They are also known to take Brown Hawkers *Aeshna grandis*, a species that is about the same size as its consumer. In Australia, the Blue Skimmer *Orthetrum caledonicum* has been seen feeding on the Dune Ringtail *Austrolestes minjerriba* damselfly and on the Scarlet Percher *Diplacodes haematodes*, a fellow libellulid. These are just some examples. With Dragonflies, even cannibalism is an option – this has been seen in Blue-tailed Damselflies *Ischnura elegans*, Club-tailed Dragonflies *Gomphus vulgatissimus* and Common Green Darners *Anax junius*, to give just three examples.

How big and how much?

Many prey items consumed by Dragonflies are much smaller than the Dragonfly itself. But at the other end of the scale, their victims can be quite substantial. The Black-tailed Skimmer *Orthetrum cancellatum* sometimes feeds on Copper Demoiselles *Calopteryx haemorrhoidalis*. The demoiselle can be as much as 40 per cent of the weight of the skimmer. The Eastern Pondhawk *Erythemis simplicicollis*, which is found in North America, is even more notable. It will take a Blue Dasher *Pachydiplax longipennis*, another libellulid, which can weigh over 60 per cent of the pondhawk's weight.

On average, however, it has been estimated that a Dragonfly eats about 20 per cent of its own weight every day. As mentioned above, for some species at least, it can be more than this. But it does, of course, depend on how much of the victim is consumed.

A Dragonfly's Diet

Aphids

Cicadas

Pond skaters/Water strider

Alderflies

Beetles

Scorpionflies

Caddisflies

Butterflies and moths

Wasps

Flying ants

Honey bees

Bumble bees

Damselflies

True dragonflies

Herbivores?

From time to time people see Dragonflies eating plant material. Why they do this is unclear. Some damselflies have been seen apparently trying to take plant galls. Perhaps they were actually trying to get at the insects inside the galls.

Specialist feeders

Specialist feeders are rare among Dragonflies. The Forest Giants are spider devotees and are the best example. There are also some Skimmer *Orthetrum* species that are particularly keen on eating butterflies.

Temporary specialisms are also known, when a species exploits one food source for a time, but then switches back to a more diverse diet. One unfortunate example of this can occur when hungry Dragonflies discover beehives. This happened in Louisiana in the 1940s and has apparently happened elsewhere as well. Such was the impact of Regal Darners *Coryphaeschna ingens* and Common Green Darners *Anax junius* in Louisiana that they were given the nickname of 'bee-butchers'.

Some surprising meals

- There is a record from Denmark of the Brown Hawker *Aeshna grandis* taking small frogs off the ground. The Brown Hawker is usually a midair feeder.
- An unidentified hawker-like species was seen feeding on a dead slug on a road.
- The Common Blue Damselfly *Enallagma cyathigerum* has been seen feeding underwater! The individual concerned was probably egg-laying at the time, but didn't miss the opportunity to eat some Willow Aphids *Tuberolachnus salignus* while it was down there.
- In North America, a Stream Bluet *Enallagma exsulsans* managed to add pond skaters to its diet, but it did take about 20 attempts before it managed to catch one.

Opposite left: The pondhawks often take substantial prey items. This Eastern Pondhawk *Erythemis simplicicollis*, a North American Dragonfly, is dining out on a butterfly.

Dragonflies as prey

Predators they may be, but that doesn't stop Dragonflies becoming prey, and not just at the legs and mandibles of other Dragonflies.

Birds are probably the Dragonfly's most significant enemy. In Europe, the Hobby *Falco subbuteo* is a well-known catcher of Dragonflies. A Hobby is agile enough to take a Dragonfly in midair and to pull off the insect's wings after capturing it while still remaining airborne. Eleven species of Dragonfly are known to have succumbed to this dashing falcon, and when it has chicks to feed, a Hobby can take 70 Dragonflies in an hour. Other birds of prey take them too, including Sharp-shinned Hawks *Accipiter striatus*, Merlins *Falco columbarius* and American Kestrels *F. sparverius* in North America, which make the most of migrating swarms of Dragonflies.

Bee-eaters *Merops apiaster* eat plenty of Dragonflies, and those that breed in France have been found to be particularly adept at grabbing tandem pairs of darters. Swallows and rollers take them, and, sometimes, so do Great Spotted Woodpeckers *Dendrocopus major*. This unlikely Dragonfly-eater has been recorded feeding true dragonflies to its young in Germany. Research published in 2010 found that Dragonflies and other large insects were an important part of the diet of migrating Aquatic Warblers *Acrocephalus paludicola* in France. A more comprehensive list of birds that eat Dragonflies is included in the box (right).

Other predators

Many Dragonflies, especially damselflies, come to a sticky end in spiders' webs and there are also lizards, frogs and fish that eat Dragonflies. At least 33 Yellow-Spotted Dragonflies

Some Birds that Eat Dragonflies

Ducks

Herons

Birds of prey including: Hobby, Amur Falcon *Falco amurensis*, Merlin, American Kestrel, Sharp-shinned Hawk and Swainson's Hawk *Buteo swainsoni*

Waders

Nightjars

Bee-eaters

Rollers

Great Spotted Woodpecker

Old World flycatchers

Tyrant flycatchers

Swallows

Wagtails

Chaffinch *Fringilla coelebs*

Aquatic Warbler

Sedge Warbler *Acrocephalus schoenobaenus*

Reed Warbler *Acrocephalus scirpaceus* (the one pictured above has taken a damselfly to feed its young)

Icterids

Procordulia grayi ended up inside a trout in New Zealand. Some fish will jump out of the water to grab a Dragonfly snack, but they don't always need to jump.

On 5 July, 2010, I found an Emperor *Anax imperator* floundering in the water at Wicken Fen in Cambridgeshire, England. I suspect it ended up there after a territorial tussle. I watched it for about 15 minutes, during which it was attacked by fish several times. The attacks could be sudden and violent, dragging the Emperor underwater. When it managed to pull itself out of the water up a plant stem, which it did more than once, I realized that the end of its abdomen was missing – presumably the fish had eaten it. Eventually, the insect stopped moving its legs and appeared to have died, lying on its back in the water – a head, a thorax, wings, and what was left of its abdomen.

Egg-laying can be a dangerous time for Dragonflies. They are vulnerable to attack from aquatic bugs (Hemiptera), Whirligig Beetles, Raft Spiders and fish.

Robber flies pluck damselflies and smaller true dragonflies out of midair. Scorpion flies eat damselflies. Wasps and bees sometimes sting and decapitate damselflies, before sucking out the victim's fluids, and Hornets will tackle prey as large as a Southern Hawker *Aeshna cyanea*. In the United States, Common Green Darners *Anax junius* have ended their lives as food for the Little Brown Bat *Myotis lucifugus*.

But the ones that meet the most dramatic end may well be those who finish their brief, glorious, airborne days in the jaws of a crocodile. The smaller species that perish in sundews (a type of insectivorous plant) have a rather gentler demise.

Above: These pond skaters *Gerris* sp. are feeding on an unfortunate Azure Damselfly *Coenagrion puella*.

Below: Mission accomplished – this Robber-fly (Asilidae) is eating a White-legged Damselfly *Platycnemis pennipes*.

Staying alive

A Dragonfly's supreme powers of flight, coupled with its excellent eyesight, are among its best defences – it can outfly many would-be predators. Not being seen is another good way to avoid getting eaten. Still Dragonflies can be hard to see and egg-laying females can be easily overlooked. The Gray Petaltail *Tachopteryx thoreyi*, a large Dragonfly that lives in North America, demonstrates Dragonfly camouflage at its best (take a look at the photo on the opposite page). Some damselflies settle on plant stems that are narrow enough to allow their eyes to protrude to the sides of the stem. If necessary, they just shuffle around to the other side.

The Ebony Jewelwing *Calopteryx maculata*, a North American species, is a favourite meal of the Dragonhunter *Hagenius brevistylus*, an impressive clubtail. To increase its life expectancy, a jewelwing will stop moving when it realizes a Dragonhunter is settled nearby.

Some species take immobility to another level and play dead to protect themselves. This has been seen in the Barbet Percher *Diplacodes luminans*,

Several damselflies have been caught by the sticky hairs of this sundew *Drosera* sp. and will provide additional nutrients for the plant.

The Gray Petaltail *Tachopteryx thoreyi* is a North American master of camouflage.

found in South Africa, and in the Common Blue Damselfy *Enallagma cyathigerum* and the Blue-tailed Damselfly *Ischnura elegans*.

Few Dragonflies adopt mimicry as a defensive strategy, although there are libellulids in Africa that can be mistaken for bees, and female

Broad-bodied Chasers *Libellula depressa* do a fair impression of a flying Hornet.

And if they do get caught, the bigger species can bite, and some use their claspers to make their presence felt.

Above: Female and immature male Broad-bodied Chasers *Libellula depressa* are hornet look-alikes.

Parasites

Take a close look at an adult Dragonfly, particularly a damselfly, and you could see small orange or red blobs on the thorax or abdomen. These are water mites, parasites that feed on the Dragonfly's haemolymph. Some attach themselves as larvae to Dragonfly larvae underwater, and then switch to the adult when it emerges. Others have land-based larvae that find their way on to the water surface and then on to the adult insect. Parasites do seem to affect the fitness of their hosts. One study with the Azure Damselfly *Coenagrion puella* found that while they mated no less frequently, they laid fewer fertilized eggs.

Below: The water mites on the thorax of this male Emerald Damselfly *Lestes sponsa* are very easy to see.

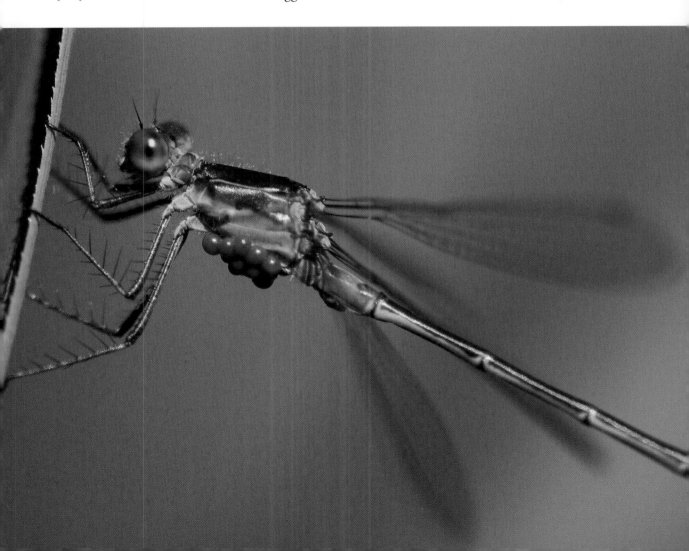

5 | The mating game

Producing offspring is the aim of every adult Dragonfly. Achieving this aim involves finding a mate, mating successfully and laying eggs in an appropriate place. Even when all that is done, there is no guarantee that any of the eggs will survive to become larvae, or that any of the larvae will survive to become the next generation of breeding adults.

Dragonfly territories

Not all Dragonfly species are territorial. Those that are include most of the true dragonflies and the demoiselles. A territory is an area that a male defends against other males of the same species. Some Dragonflies are so territorial that they defend their patch against other species too. The Four-spotted Chaser *Libellula quadrimaculata* is a feisty creature and, in Europe, will take on the much larger Emperor *Anax imperator* should one dare to venture into its territory. Dragonfly expert Norman Moore, however, suggested that when the bout is between different species, it might be more like sparring than the genuine conflict that occurs between individuals of the same species.

Typically, when a male defends a territory, he is protecting an area with good egg-laying opportunities. The Australian Emperor *Hemianax papuensis* has been known to defend an area of about 5,000 sq m. At the other end of the scale, the territory of *Copera annulata*, a damselfly of China, Japan and Korea, has been measured at just 0.1 sq m. For some species, a territory is a length of riverbank or lakeside that is patrolled. Its length could be as much as 92m in the case of the Common Baskettail *Epitheca cynosura*, a North American species, and as little as a metre for the Blue-faced Darner *Coryphaeschna adnexa*, another North American species. Territories are not necessarily static – generally, as more males of the same species arrive, the territories get smaller. Common Darters *Sympetrum striolatum* like a sunny territory – and will move their territory to make the most of sunny patches.

Most Dragonflies meet their partner at the egg-laying site, whether they are a territorial species or not. A good territory will include good places to lay eggs. This is what the females are looking for, so the territory

Pages 82–83: These are Variable Damselflies *Coenagrion pulchellum* in tandem. The author took this photograph on 2 June, 2012, in Cambridgeshire, England.

Opposite right: Common Baskettails *Epitheca cynosura* are very impressive fliers. Their territorial patrol flights can include extended periods of hovering.

should receive a good number of female visitors and, as it is his patch, the territory holder should have plenty of mating opportunities.

Territorial ownership can be very brief, at just a few minutes – or much longer. *Megaloprepus coerulatus*, one of the Forest Giants, has been known to use the same territory over a 90-day period, and in South Africa, the Painted Sprite *Pseudagrion hageni*, a pond damselfly, came back to the same patch every day for 39 days. A male may not have the exclusive use of a particular territory – at different times of the day, different males may claim it as their own.

Even in territorial species, not all males will secure a territory, but that doesn't necessarily rule out mating. Some seek out females in feeding areas. Some become 'wanderers' who fly into territories in the hope of finding an available female. Some become 'satellites' and loiter unobtrusively in someone else's territory waiting for an opportunity. In the Common Darter *Sympetrum striolatum*, males without territories hang around near an occupied territory. Sooner or later the territory holder will be busy mating, at which point the nearest male moves in and becomes the territory holder.

The Painted Sprite *Pseudagrion hagenia* can be seen in South Africa in some very shady habitats. It has been known to return to the same patch daily for over five weeks.

The Common Whitetail *Plathemis lydia*, a very common North American species, has a dynamic system of territory ownership. In this species, a number of males occupy the same territory. The dominant male takes control around the middle of the day, which is prime mating time. As he ages, he drops down the hierarchy and is replaced by a male in the prime of life. The closer they are to their prime, the higher they will be in the hierarchy.

In Fiji, some *Nesobasis* damselflies do things very differently – it is the females who defend the territory.

Resolving conflict

Holding a territory is not just about mating priority – the territory holder must be prepared to challenge intruders too. When an intruder enters an occupied territory, he may just spot the owner and move on, but things are not always that simple. Once the interloper has been spotted, steps will be taken to speed his departure. A perched territory holder might start proceedings with a threat display, showing off bold wing markings, or brightly coloured legs, eyes or abdomen, for example. But more often than not, the defender takes to the wing. A typical encounter might go something like this…

The owner-occupier flies straight at his unwelcome guest, from one side or from underneath. If a chase is required to secure eviction, the territory holder flies lower than the intruder. Colours and markings may also be used to intimidate. The intruder may not give up easily and things can get more heated. The two males may square up to each other, buzz each other again and again, circle each other, or spiral down, with clashing wings, each male trying to get beneath his opponent. A fight can result in damaged wings and bites to the thorax and head. A combatant may even end up in the water (see page 77). At its most extreme, one of the fighters will be killed.

Essentially, there are four components in a Dragonfly's aggressive behaviour – flying at the intruder, the chase, threat displays and actual fighting. Any one encounter may not involve all of them and they may not occur in that order.

Dragonflies employ various types of threat displays. The White-legged Damselfly *Platycnemis pennipes* shows off its white legs in flight and uses them in courtship displays, too. The Scarlet Skimmer *Crocothemis servilia*, an Asian species that has been introduced to North America, will bend its abdomen up as a threat display. The Boulder Jewel *Platycypha fitzsimonsi*, a South African damselfly, displays the white inner surfaces of its legs and, like White-legged Damselflies, his legs are courtship tools as well. And not to be outdone, the Twelve-spotted Skimmer *Libellula pulchella*, a North American species, settles territorial

Male Common Whitetails *Plathemis lydia* share territorial space, and move up the hierarchy as they approach their prime.

clashes with aerobatics – the prize goes to the one that flies vertical rings around the other.

Normally, the owner-occupier is the winner. Males don't always get it right. Sometimes a female is attacked in error, but when the male realizes his mistake, he changes his behaviour…

Attracting a mate

Typically, it is the damselflies that engage in courtship displays, with the males doing their best to impress by showing off a brightly coloured or boldly marked body part. A male Boulder Jewel tries to win a mating by hovering near a potential partner and showing her his bright white legs. Male Banded Demoiselles *Calopteryx splendens* flick their wings as they fly past females. Sometimes they make it very clear where the eggs should be laid by rushing to the water surface and landing briefly, with the tip of the abdomen bent up so that the female can see the whitish 'tail-light' on its underside. Different species of demoiselles have different coloured tail-lights. Those of the Copper Demoiselle *C. haemorroidalis* are reddish-pink. Those of the Beautiful Demoiselle *C. virgo* are reddish or brown. These give a female a clear signal of the male's identity.

The Copper Demoiselle has another trick in its repertoire. It lands on the water and lets the current carry it a little way, presumably to show the female the strength of the current, which may reveal something significant about the quality of the egg-laying site.

There are other species that show off the egg-laying site, including some true dragonflies. But for the most part, true dragonflies don't bother with courtship. If a female arrives at the egg-laying site, they just grab hold of her and, all being well, mate. Females are in demand, and males may fight to secure a breeding opportunity when a female makes an appearance.

Mating

Normally, males arrive at the egg-laying site before females, and it is here that the mating process begins. Accepting a male's advance is not compulsory. If you see an airborne female hawker or damselfly at a breeding site with the back end of her abdomen pointing straight down, you are looking at a female that is giving a very clear signal that she is not interested. If she is willing, the pair gets 'in tandem'. First, the male's legs take hold of the female's thorax. Then he bends his abdomen so that his claspers can grab hold of either her head (true dragonflies) or the front end of her thorax (damselflies). At this point his legs can let go of her thorax and the pair are in tandem.

In true dragonflies, the males have three appendages – two upper and one lower – that they use to grab hold of the female. These grip the female tightly, with the upper appendages to the rear and the lower appendage on the front of her head. It is not unusual for this vice-like grip to damage and scar the female's eyes.

Typically, true dragonflies don't go in for courtship displays, but damselflies do. This male Beautiful Demoiselle *Calopteryx virgo* (with the darker pigmented wings) is performing for the female in the foreground.

Damselflies have four appendages, two above and two below. They grip the female on the thorax, not the head, taking hold of her at the rear of the front segment of the thorax. The area he grips is called the pronotum. The shape of the pronotum differs from one damselfly species to another. The theory is that, in any given species, the male's claspers will only fit the pronotums of females of the same species. Mostly it works. In true dragonflies, the female's head shape works with the male's claspers in a similar way.

Male Dragonflies, unlike any other insects, are endowed with two sets of genitalia. Before mating can occur, a male must transfer sperm from his primary genitalia (near the rear of his abdomen) to his secondary or accessory genitalia (near the front of his abdomen). Typically, true dragonflies make the transfer before they grab hold of a female, and damselflies do it as soon as they are in tandem.

For the sperm to be passed to the female, her genital opening needs to make contact with his secondary genitalia. To enable this to happen, he curves his abdomen down and she bends hers up. Together, the mating pair forms an imperfect heart-shape known as 'the wheel position' or 'heart position'. Some Dragonfly-watchers refer to it as being 'in cop' (in copula). Mating can last just seconds, minutes or sometimes over an hour. The Blue-tailed Damselfly *Ischnura elegans* is known to have been in cop for as long as eight hours. Typically, mating takes place tucked away in the vegetation or in a tree, either in the territory or away from it. Sometimes mating takes place on the wing. Damselflies especially can be quite easy to see in the heart position.

Below: When a male damselfly such as this Small Red Damselfly *Ceriagrion tenellum* (top) takes hold of a female for mating, he grips the thorax. When a true dragonfly (bottom, Common Hawker *Aeshna juncea*) takes hold, he grips the head.

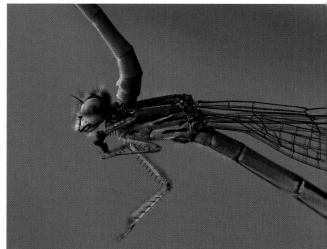

Mating takes place in the 'wheel position' or 'heart position', as shown here by Red Saddlebags *Tramea onusta*, a North American dragonfly (left) and the White-legged Damselfly *Platycnemis pennipes*, a European species (below).

Unlike aggressive territorial encounters where the male typically flies at the interloper from underneath or from one side, when the 'interloper' is a female, the male moves in from above.

Mature males at a breeding site can seize the moment, and the female, whenever they appear. A female needs more recovery time, and has to wait one to five days after laying her eggs before the next clutch is ready.

Assuring fatherhood

A Dragonfly's penis is part of its secondary genitalia and does more than you might imagine. After mating, a female Dragonfly stores sperm before using it. When a male mates, he wants it to be his sperm that the female uses and not that of some other male. So, before he deposits his own, he does what he can to remove any that is already there. He uses his penis to do this. He may pull out the sperm on

You can tell that this male Scarce Chaser *Libellula fulva* has mated – the female's legs have rubbed some of the pruinosity off of his abdomen.

backward-pointing hooks or with other structures on his penis. Or he may push or flush the sperm further in – to places that the female will probably not retrieve it from. Some species will even stimulate the female so that she squeezes stored sperm out of places that are beyond his reach, so that he can then remove it.

This fascinating aspect of Dragonfly reproductive biology was discovered by Jonathan Waage, who worked with the Ebony Jewelwing *Calopteryx maculata*, a North American damselfly, to confirm his suspicion.

Egg-laying and guarding

To protect his genetic investment, a male may remain in tandem with the female while she is laying her eggs. This makes sure that another male does not displace his sperm and is called 'guarding'. Some males guard without being in tandem – they stay close by and do their best to see off any male that threatens their investment. One advantage of 'detached guarding' is that the male is free to grab another female and sow his seeds there, too. He can also guard more than one female at the same time. *Cora semiopaca*, a stunning Latin American damselfly with glittering

By egg-laying in tandem, this male Small Red-eyed Damselfly *Erythromma viridulum* ensures that no other males get in on the act before the eggs are laid.

blue patches on dark-tipped wings, has been known to guard five females at once. Not all females are guarded, however – some lay their eggs alone.

Whether the female is guarded or not, there are two main approaches to egg-laying – endophytically, which means 'within plants', and exophytically, which means 'outside of plants'.

The Dragonflies that lay their eggs 'into plants' are the damselflies, the hawkers/darners, the petaltails, the redspots and *Epiophlebia*. These species have ovipositors that can cut their way into plant material and make an opening to lay their eggs into. The eggs themselves are not spherical – their shape is more sausage-like, which is a good shape for eggs that are laid into something, as opposed to onto something. Endophytic species lay their eggs one at a time, at a rate of up to just over 20 eggs a minute, in a variety of places, including plant stems, sodden logs, mud and sometimes tree trunks. Damselflies lay their eggs in distinctive arrangements – you can identify the species from the arrangement of the eggs. A female may lower herself down a plant stem and go completely underwater to lay her eggs (see image on page 94), and may take a guarding male with her. Some can be submerged for a surprisingly long time – a Beautiful Demoiselle *Calopteryx virgo* was submerged for just over two hours.

The other true dragonflies are exophytic. Look for females, in tandem or solo, flying low and dipping the tip of their abdomen to the surface of the water. The vast majority of these females lay

Above: An Emerald Damselfly *Lestes sponsa* is egg-laying into a plant stem.

Below: The damselflies and hawkers are endophytic – they lay their eggs into plants. This is a Black Emperor *Anax tristis*, a huge African hawker.

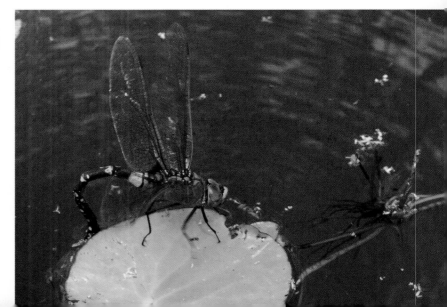

eggs that are much rounder and more lemon-shaped than those of the endophytes. They lay them in quantities on the water surface or nearby. The Blue Dasher *Pachydiplax longipennis*, a North American libellulid, has been known to lay as many as 700 eggs in just 35 seconds and there are species that lay nearly 1,700 eggs in a minute. Once they hit the water, the eggs of some exophytic species sink to the bottom. Some species produce eggs that are coated in 'jelly'. This can be sticky and glues the eggs to plants or rocks, which stops them being carried downstream by the current.

Not all exophytes lay their eggs onto water. The Ruddy Darter *Sympetrum sanguineum*, a European species, sometimes lays its drought-tolerant eggs on mud or grass that is not underwater (see image opposite). All being well, these areas flood in winter, at which point the eggs hatch.

This Large Red Damselfly *Pyrrhosoma nymphula* has submerged herself completely to lay her eggs.

Tandem guarding occurs among endophytic and exophytic species. In some exophytic species, the male helps the female to shed her eggs by flicking her downwards so that the eggs are rinsed off by the water, or simply thrown off.

Ruddy Darters *Sympetrum sanguineum* are exophytic – they don't lay their eggs into plants. They don't always lay them onto water either.

Safety in numbers

Sometimes groups of females, either while in tandem or not, are seen laying their eggs in close proximity to each other. Research has found that the presence of one egg-laying female lures in others. The reason for this could be safety in numbers – if you are of a group of egg-laying damselflies and a hungry frog takes a female from the group, the odds are that it isn't you. And if a frog takes one of your neighbours, you can fly away from trouble.

Basket cases

Baskettails (*Epitheca* species) are found in North America, Europe and Asia. The female produces a line of eggs, which collects in a mass of as many as 2,000 eggs at the tip of her abdomen. She deposits it on plants just above the water surface – one end sticks and the mass unwinds and expands. One line of eggs can be 1cm long. The eggs stay high in the water and get plenty of warmth and plenty of oxygen. Algae may invade the strand – this might sound like bad news, but by photosynthesizing, the algae provide extra oxygen for the eggs.

Flicking eggs

Some species, such as the Keeled Skimmer *Orthetrum coerulescens*, for example, scoop up a bit of water and toss this and their eggs to the waterside or at plants.

Egg sizes and quantities

A small Dragonfly egg measures about 0.5 x 0.2mm. A big one measures about 0.7 x 0.6mm.

Below: Here, a group of White Featherlegs *Platycnemis latipes* is egg-laying in tandem. White Featherlegs are found in France, Spain and Portugal.

Opposite: Common Darter *Sympetrum striolatum* eggs (top) and Southern Hawker *Aeshna cyanea* eggs (bottom). The hawker's more elongated eggs are a better shape for inserting into plants than the darter's, which are laid into water.

On average, a female Azure Damselfly *Coenagrion puella* lays just less than four clutches of eggs – small clutches contain just over 100 eggs and big clutches contain about 400. The theory is that if she lays eggs every day for 15 days, she could deposit about 4,200 eggs.

In contrast, some libellulids lay almost 2,000 eggs in just one clutch.

No males

The Citrine Forktail *Ischnura hastata* is largely a damselfly of the Americas. They are also found on the Galapagos Islands in the Pacific and on the Azores, a group of islands way out in the Atlantic Ocean west of Portugal. The Azorean individuals were originally misidentified as Marsh Bluetails *Ischnura senegalensis*. In 1938, 63 specimens were collected – Valle wrote about them saying that, unfortunately, they were all females. The misidentification was spotted by Jean Belle in 1982, and in 1988 he collected over 30 specimens, but he didn't find any males. It was these specimens that led to their correct identification by Jan van Tol. It seems that Citrine Forktails on the Azores reproduce parthenogenetically. This means that the eggs become adults without any male involvement. Fertilization is not required and generation after generation is entirely female. These are no other Dragonflies in the world where this is known to occur.

The Scarce Blue-tailed Damselfly *Ischnura pumilio* is the only other damselfly species on the Azores – sometimes these males are seen in tandem with Citrine Forktails.

Unusual egg-laying sites

Loitering near a pond could result in unwanted attention from a Southern Hawker *Aeshna cyanea*. This European species has been known to try to lay eggs in a rubber boot, a dog, someone's arm, someone's ankle, someone's calf, someone's thigh, someone's jumper and a Yellow-bellied Toad *Bombina variegata*.

A Fawn Darner *Boyeria vinosa* used its ovipositor to cut a hole in someone's arm!

Right: No Citrine Forktail *Ischnura hastata* males have been found in the Azorean population of this very small damselfly. The population seems to perpetuate itself without males.

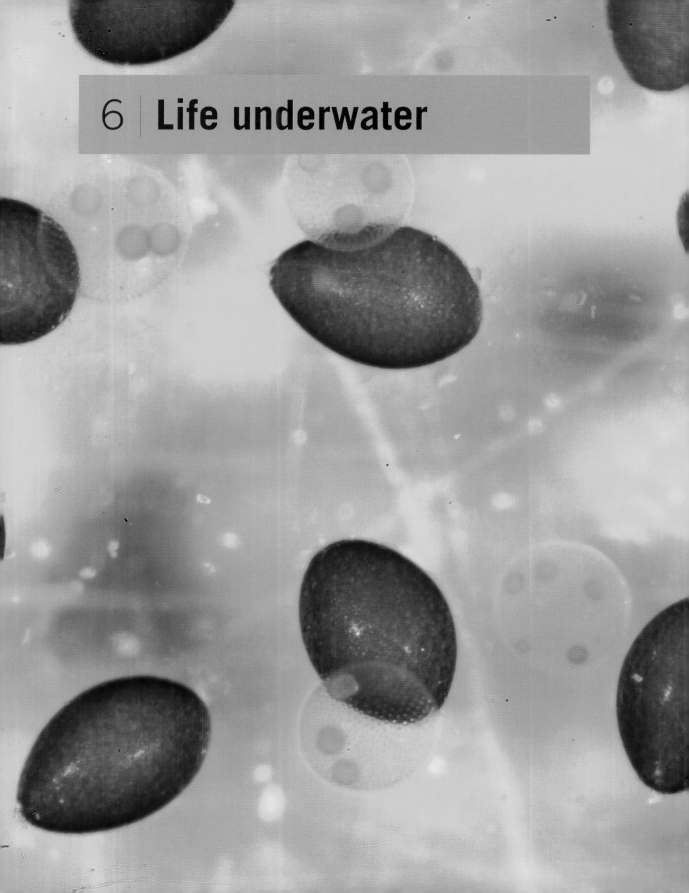

6 | Life underwater

Most people are much more familiar with the adult phase of a Dragonfly's life cycle than its time as a larva underwater. Yet, in temperate regions, a Dragonfly spends more time underwater than in the air, though the reverse can be true in the tropics and subtropics.

What happens to all those eggs?

Of the large numbers of eggs laid, only a minority survive to become the next generation of adult Dragonflies. To make it to that stage, the tiny package containing a potential Dragonfly has to hatch, make its way to water if it isn't there already, and avoid being eaten during its time underwater and its emergence. Most don't make it – an English study of Azure Damselflies *Coenagrion puella* estimated that nearly 99 per cent succumbed along the way.

Some eggs end their life as food for snails or fish, but it is probable that more are killed by tiny wasps. These include some of the smallest known insects – some are the size of a speck of dust. Infestation can reach very high levels with, in some situations, over 90 per cent of the eggs being affected. The wasps lay their eggs inside the Dragonfly egg and the wasp's offspring then eat the Dragonfly egg from inside it. The wasps use some impressive tactics to get their eggs into position. Some get underwater and hunt out the eggs. Some find eggs that have been laid over the water. Others are small enough to mate inside the Dragonfly's egg!

The time from egg-laying to hatching can be surprisingly brief – as little as five days in the Globe Skimmer *Pantala flavescens* and the Blue Dasher *Pachydiplax longipennis* – although it typically takes from one to three or four weeks. Most of the time, development begins very soon after the eggs are laid, but not always. Some species use diapause, when development stops or slows down, to maximize their offspring's chances of survival. This strategy works well when eggs are laid at the end of the summer or later – if development and hatching were to follow straight on, the first larval stages would have to endure a cold winter. Eggs can be in diapause for 80 days or longer – an egg of a Common Hawker *Aeshna juncea* was in diapause for over 360 days.

Pages 100–101: For a Dragonfly, life underwater begins as an egg. These are Common Darter *Sympetrum striolatum* eggs.

The tropical dry season presents a different challenge, and eggs seem to be able to help a species survive this, too. In these cases, it is thought that the embryo develops but that hatching is delayed.

What comes out of the egg?

Often a Dragonfly's life cycle is simplified as egg–larva–adult–egg. This misses out one vital if short-lived stage – the prolarva.

The prolarva is what comes out of the egg. It can leap and squirm, and its job is to get to water, which is often where it finds itself on hatching anyway. But that isn't always the case. The Willow Emerald *Lestes viridis* damselfly is unusual among its near relatives in that it lays its eggs in twigs and branches over water. When things go well, its prolarvae simply fall into the water. When things don't go well, however, the prolarvae find themselves on the ground and have to make their way to water. Prolarvae are not able to walk or swim, but they can have remarkable jumping abilities – one leap from the prolarva of the Japanese Relict Dragonfly *Epiophlebia superstes* can take it about 100 times further than its own length.

These are Red-eyed Damselfly *Erythromma najas* larvae. This species breeds in still water and slow-flowing waterways and is normally a larva for two years before the adult is ready to emerge.

When it gets to water, a prolarva's job is done. It moults and a very small true larva takes to the water. The prolarva may have survived for just seconds or perhaps an hour or two. Those of *Aeschnophlebia longistigma*, an Asian species, can make it to 14 hours.

And then there are larvae

Like the adults, the larvae of damselflies and true dragonflies take different forms. Those of damselflies are typically long and relatively thin, with three external tail-like gills (different families have differently shaped gills). True dragonfly larvae are stouter, with no external gills. Some have long bodies; others are more spider-like in appearance.

A true dragonfly's gills are tucked away in its rectum. Whether internal or external, the gills take oxygen from the water for respiration. In true dragonflies, muscular action sucks water into – and pushes it out of – the rectum, allowing oxygen to be taken on board and carbon dioxide to be removed.

A damselfly's gills are also used in locomotion – a swish of the tail propels the beast forward. This works well in those species that have flat gills, but it is not as effective in all damselflies. The gills of a demoiselle/jewelwing, for example, are triangular in cross section rather than flat. These larvae are not good swimmers.

A true dragonfly larva is jet-propelled. The water it takes into its rectum can be squirted out, pushing the larva forward at quite a pace.

Other respiratory apparatus

A damselfly's main respiratory tool is its gills, but damselflies also move water in and out of the rectum. The inside of the rectum has many tracheae (tubes for transporting oxygen) and is thought to play a part in respiration, but there are no internal gills.

Bannerwing (Polythoridae) and Gossamerwing (Euphaeidae) larvae have seven pairs of gills on the sides of the abdomen as well as the three gills at its tip. Amphipterygidae larvae (a broad-winged damselfly family) have two gill tufts near the anus.

Dragonflies are also able to take oxygen onboard through other parts of their body surface.

Damselfly larvae have three external gills at the end of their abdomen, which are used in locomotion as well as respiration. These are the gills of a Common Blue Damselfly *Enallagma cyathigerum*.

How to breathe when buried in mud

Some true dragonflies spend most of their larval life immersed in mud beneath the water. They need to eat and breathe, so they keep their head and backside out of the mud. Some take things further – their last two abdominal segments are very long and work as a 'breathing tube'.

Lestinogomphus africanus, an African clubtail, goes to quite a length to get water to its gills – its breathing tube is about 60mm long.

What do Dragonfly larvae eat?

Like the winged predators that those who survive will become, Dragonfly larvae are ferocious carnivores. Non-biting midge larvae and water fleas can be particularly important food items, but Dragonfly larvae are not picky eaters – mostly, they will eat whatever prey is unfortunate enough to come their way. Their diet sheet also includes other fly larvae (mosquitoes, biting midges, midges, meniscus midges and black-flies), leeches, flatworms, crustaceans, stonefly nymphs, mayfly larvae, beetle larvae, caddisfly larvae, water mites, adult beetles and flies, protozoa, rotifers, snails and their eggs, spiders, tadpoles, fish eggs and even small fish! In a rare break from 'carnivory', a 1990 study in India added phytoplankton to the list.

Not all prey is caught underwater – some is taken from the water surface. Hawker larvae have been known to make a meal of an egg-laying damselfly or a pond skater.

A Southern Hawker *Aeshna cyanea* larva is eating a bloodworm (a non-biting midge larva). Its extendable 'mask' (see page 108) is very obvious.

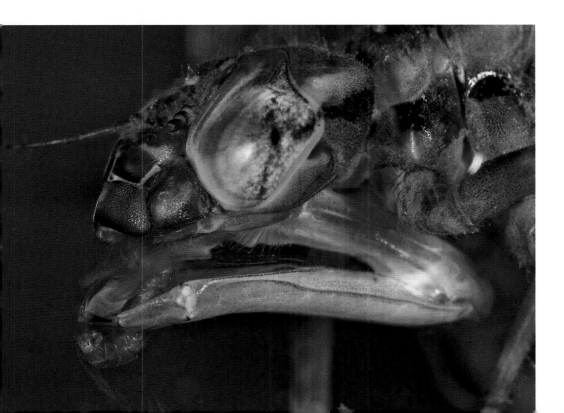

Cannibalism

Whether it is a different species or not, one Dragonfly larvae may end its days as food for another. However, there is usually a size difference of at least two moults when a larva eats another individual of the same species.

Hunting techniques

Dragonfly larvae employ a range of hunting techniques. A species may have a preferred hunting method, but different approaches may be adopted at different times. In broad terms, there are larvae that hunt among submerged aquatic plants and larvae that lurk at the bottom, hidden among rotting leaves or in mud or sand. Those that hunt among plants are 'claspers', 'sprawlers' or a bit of both. Hawkers tend to be claspers, holding on to a plant stem a little beneath the surface of the water. These larvae are elongated and torpedo-like, which is a good shape for moving around in a clump of plants. They have big eyes and use sight to detect their prey. Dragonfly larvae often just wait for their next meal to come to them, but sometimes a hawker will stalk its prey.

This is a very young Southern Hawker *Aeshna cyanea* larva. Its form is quite different to that of the damselfly larvae on page 103.

Darters (*Sympetrum* species) are good examples of sprawlers. Sprawlers are also found a little below the surface, loafing on plants with their legs to the sides. They are less elongate, have smaller eyes than hawkers, and use sight and touch to find their prey.

The chasers and skimmers are 'hiders'. They live at the bottom, hidden, and rely on touch, via their antennae or legs, to get a meal. Not surprisingly, their eyes are small. Typical hiders have shorter, broader abdomens. They are hairy, relatively flat and have powerful legs to help them dig. Many clubtail larvae also use their antennae as 'spades'.

Goldenring larvae are burrowers. They are very hairy, with long bodies and small eyes. They kick their way in to the bottom substrate and lie in wait, having made themselves very hard to see. All that is visible is the tip of the abdomen, their antennae and their eyes. They use touch to locate their prey.

Normally, it is the movement of a potential prey item that gives away its presence to a hungry Dragonfly larva. Having said that, the Emperor *Anax imperator* is one species that has been known to dine out on snails, which, at best, are barely moving.

Larvae in the dry

The larvae of the vast majority of Dragonfly species live in water, but there are exceptions. Those of most petaltail species dig a deep burrow that becomes their home for five years or more. The larvae spend their days covered in mud and come to the entrance of their burrow to ambush a passing meal – a terrestrial spider perhaps. These larvae are semi-terrestrial and can survive out of water for a very long time. The New Zealand Bush Giant Dragonfly *Uropetala carovei* is one of them. It lives in a chamber that has some water in it and needs damp air to breathe, but can breathe air for months at a time.

The larvae of the Golden-ringed Dragonfly *Cordulegaster boltonii* are burrowers.

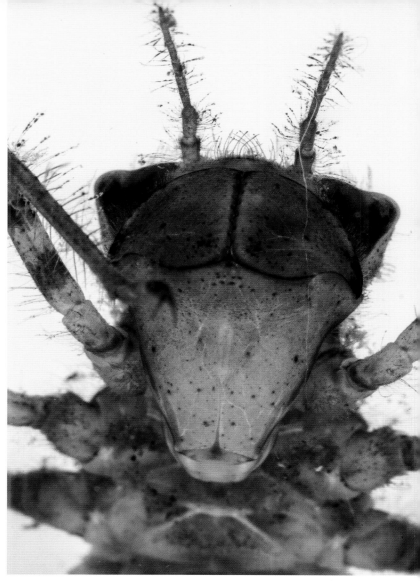

The Tropical Rockmaster *Diphlebia euphoeoides*, a damselfly of Queensland, Australia and New Guinea, has larvae that can cope with life in dried-out streams and rivers. And the larvae of the Oahu Damselfly *Megalagrion oahuense*, a Hawaiian endemic previously mentioned on page 44, live entirely on dry land.

The mask that kills

The photo on this page shows a Dragonfly's 'mask'. The mask is its prey-catching device – a pair of pincers at the end of an extendable, hinged 'lower lip' that can shoot out, grab and pull back in a split second, using hydraulic pressure to drive it forward, and muscles to retract it. Mostly, the mask is held folded under the larva's head. When a larva attacks, it raises its haemolymph pressure, shuts off the opening to its rectum so that water can't be pushed out, and releases the 'safety catch' that would otherwise hold the mask in place. The mask rockets forward and the pincers can hit their target in 15 to 40 milliseconds or less. After a successful strike, the mask pulls the food back and passes it to the larva's jaws.

Many Dragonfly larvae have masks that are basically flat. Typically, however, those that are 'burrowers' or 'sprawlers' have masks that are more spoon-like. This latter category includes the emeralds (Corduliidae), the libellulids and the goldenrings.

A Brilliant Emerald *Somatochlora metallica* larva, viewed from underneath. Its folded, extendable 'mask' – which it uses to catch its prey – is easy to see.

Larvae as prey

Just like the adults, Dragonfly larvae can be prey as well as predator. Many end up as fish food. Birds eat them, including ducks, grebes, herons, waders/shorebirds and kingfishers, and so do frogs, toads, newts, snakes and turtles. There are smaller predators, too – bugs (Hemiptera), beetles, leeches and of course, other Dragonfly larvae.

A 2006 study in Wales found that Eurasian Otters *Lutra lutra* were dining out on Migrant Hawkers *Aeshna mixta* and Golden-ringed Dragonflies *Cordulegaster boltonii*. The remains of at least 66 larvae were discovered in 11 out of 18 otter spraints.

And in some parts of the world, true dragonfly larvae are taken by young crocodiles!

Self defence

To try to avoid being eaten, Dragonfly larvae adopt a number of tactics, including staying still and staying hidden. Often their colours or markings help to camouflage them.

Fleeing from the predator can work – the jet propulsion of a true dragonfly larva can help a potential victim make a rapid exit! All is not necessarily lost if the larva is caught – although a gill or leg may be. Some species donate these body parts to enable their escape and, with time, the missing bits grow back. Like the adults, some are known to play dead when trouble looms.

Larvae may also defend themselves actively. A larva may do a scorpion impression, bending the tip of the abdomen up and forwards. Building on this, a true dragonfly larva may stab the predator with the appendages at the end of its abdomen and cause enough damage to win its freedom. A Black Emperor *Anax tristis* larva is known to have drawn blood from someone's finger.

A larva's jaws can also be used in self-defence. A Common Green Darner *Anax junius* found itself in dire straits, in the mouth of a Striped Crayfish Snake *Regina alleni*. The Darner's bite drew blood from the snake and the larva lived on.

A hungry fish may be deterred from eating a larva if the larva has protective spines. Research by Petrin and others, published in 2010, found that among White-faced Darter larvae *Leucorrhinia*, the spinier species were more likely to be found in places where there were predatory fish. The less spiny species were more likely to be found in waters where there were no predatory fish. There was also variation within species – three *Leucorrhinia* species had longer spines in waters with predatory fish than they did in fish-free habitats. This suggests that the presence of fish somehow causes the larvae to grow longer spines!

It has even been suggested that larvae may make noises to defend themselves – sounds have been heard from The New Zealand Bush Giant Dragonfly *Uropetala carovei* and the Japanese Relict Dragonfly *Epiophlebia superstes*.

Moulting and growing

For a Dragonfly, its time as a larva is a time of growth. There is no other point in its life cycle when there is any appreciable change in size. A larva lives most of its life encased in a hard exoskeleton. When conditions become too cramped inside the exoskeleton, it breaks open, and a soft-bodied, wrinkly larva comes out. Without the protection of a hard exoskeleton, the larva is very vulnerable. It inflates itself while soft and can add 25 per cent to its size in a few hours, before the cuticle hardens up. Moulting also brings an additional benefit – any plants or animals that were making a living on the old exoskeleton are conveniently left behind, too.

Growth is progressive and a larva will go through moult after moult. The time from one moult to the next is called a stadium (the plural is stadia), and there are anywhere between eight and 18 of these if the prolarva is counted as one of them. The number of stadia that any given species goes through is not fixed. It can vary from one species to another, and between one individual and another of the same species. Even larvae that hatched out of the same clutch of eggs may not go through the same number of stadia as each other.

Opposite right: To grow, a Dragonfly larva must moult. Here, a soft Four-spotted Chaser *Libellula quadrimaculata* larva is leaving one exoskeleton behind to give itself room to grow. It will inflate itself while soft and then harden up to form a new exoskeleton.

The time spent as a larva is not entirely predictable either. It can be as short as 20 days, as in the Red-tipped Swampdamsel *Leptobasis vacillans*, a Latin American damselfly, or as long as seven years in the Japanese Relict Dragonfly *Epiophlebia superstes*, a cold water species. The Golden-ringed Dragonfly *Cordulegaster boltonii* can be a larva for just two years in some areas, but remains a larva for much longer further north and at greater altitude – the larval stage can last for five years or more in the UK. As a generalization, in temperate regions a Dragonfly may spend a year or two as a larva, while some tropical species spend much less time as larvae – sometimes only about a month.

Water temperature is a key factor. The Blue-tailed Damselfly *Ischnura elegans* is a common European species with an extensive range. In the

south of France, there can be two or three generations of Blue-tailed Damselflies in just one year. Things are much slower in higher latitudes in the north of Britain – here it can take two years to produce just one generation. Further south in Britain, a new generation is produced annually.

Diapause can also occur during the larval stage, postponing emergence until the conditions are right.

As a larva approaches its final moult, a number of changes occur. These are part of its metamorphosis, and include physiological changes as well as more obvious structural ones. The adult's compound eyes are developing, the larval mask is morphing into the adult labium and the wings are visible within their sheaths.

A larva will test the air a day or two before emergence begins, holding onto a stem with its front end above the water line, or in some cases, with the tip of the abdomen out in the air. It has stopped eating but is taking air into its thorax. Soon, it will really take to the air.

Voltinism

Voltinism is a word used by odonatologists. It refers to the number of generations that a Dragonfly can produce in one year.

- If it can produce one generation in a year, it is univoltine.
- If it can produce two generations in a year, it is bivoltine.
- If it can produce three generations in a year, it is trivoltine.
- If it can only produce one generation in two years, it is semivoltine.
- If it takes even longer than two years to produce one generation, it is partivoltine.

Putting larvae to work

In Burma in the 1970s, Scarlet Skimmer *Crocothemis servilia* larvae were put into open-water containers to control the numbers of yellow fever mosquitoes. The mosquito was carrying dengue fever and dengue haemorrhagic fever. The larvae did their job well, ate plenty of mosquito larvae and reduced disease transmission.

For a Dragonfly to complete its life-cycle, it must leave the water and take to the air. This Emperor *Anax imperator* larva is hauling itself up a plant stem to do just that.

7 | Up and away

If a Dragonfly survives its larval life, it is a major achievement. From then on, only one thing separates it from aerial prowess and the chance to reproduce – it must emerge.

Emergence is the adult coming out of its last larval skin. It is a risky business, a time when a Dragonfly is highly vulnerable to predation, and something that must be done right. Getting it wrong could lead to deformed wings and death.

Setting the scene

One vital ingredient for a successful emergence is finding something to emerge on – an emergence support. Most larvae choose something upright – a plant stem, a wooden post, a rock or a wall perhaps, though some choose a horizontal surface. Some true dragonflies will start looking for a suitable emergence support a few days before they actually emerge.

Darkness provides some protection from predators. Where it is warm enough, larger species of true dragonfly generally move to their emergence support under cover of darkness and take to the wing a little before

Pages 114–115: A recently emerged Golden-ringed Dragonfly *Cordulegaster boltonii* clings to the bankside. Most of its life is now behind it – this species can spend five years or more as a larva.

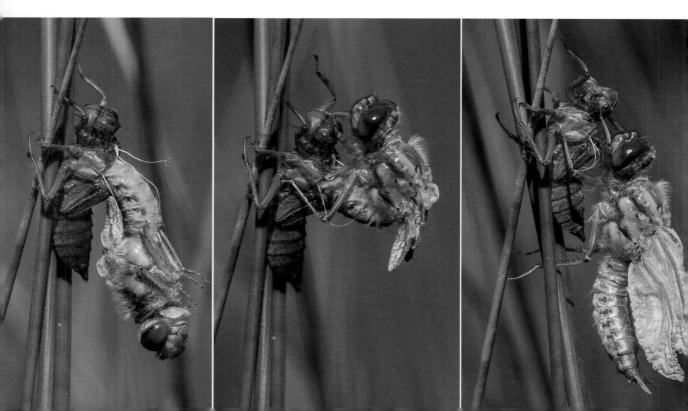

sunrise. Wherever they are, damselflies, smaller true dragonflies and – where it isn't warm enough – some of the larger ones tend to emerge in the daytime, without the protection of darkness. Typically, damselflies emerge in the morning. Many maiden flights take place early in the day. The larva may leave the water under cover of darkness, but it needs a bit more warmth to complete the process.

Emergence, once initiated, is not unstoppable. The Black-tailed Skimmer *Orthetrum cancellatum*, Common Hawker *Aeshna juncea* and Vagrant Emperor *Anax ephippiger* are known to have come out of the water at night only to find that it is too cold. They retreated to the water even though they had switched to breathing air. Emergence was postponed until the temperature was more conducive. Normally, this is just one day later, but in the Two-spotted Dragonfly *Epitheca bimaculata*, a two-day delay has been recorded. Rain can slow things down too, but it doesn't always – emergence may carry on as the rain falls.

Within a population of a given species, emergence can take place in a few days or be much more spread out. In temperate zones, a

Pages 116–117: This is a Four-spotted Chaser *Libellula quadrimaculata* emerging. Note how the wings enlarge. They are 'pumped up' with haemolymph, which is then retracted, leaving the wings with hollow veins.

synchronized spring emergence can be achieved when a population spends the winter in its final stadium. Species that spend the winter as less developed larvae need more time before they are ready to emerge. They develop quickly but emerge later and over a more protracted period. The first, synchronized emergence strategy maximizes the chance of breeding success by delivering plenty of mature adults in a short period of time. But the population could suffer badly if the weather is unsuitable. The second, protracted emergence strategy provides insurance against poor weather, but requires a sizeable population to ensure breeding success.

Getting into position

When the time is right, a larva will climb into position on its chosen emergence support. It attaches itself to it firmly, using claws on its legs. Emergence supports are not always at the water's edge. If a larva fails to find what it is looking for there, it may search further afield. An Emperor *Anax imperator* is known to have travelled over 30m from the water's edge to find a suitable support. The same species may choose a site 5m up. A Red-veined Darter *Sympetrum fonscolombei* emerged 46m from the water and a Globe Skimmer *Pantala flavescens* emerged over 12m above ground.

The normal position for emergence is with the head uppermost, but some emergences are upside-down, especially with damselflies. I have

The Green Hooktail *Paragomphus genei*, an African and European clubtail, has been known to emerge in about 20 minutes. The Yellow-legged Clubtail *Gomphus flavipes*, an Asian and European species, has done it in 15 minutes.

Opposite right: Upside-down emergence is not the norm but it does happen, particularly with damselflies. The Blue-tailed Damselfly *Ischnura elegans* (right) is one species where it is known to occur.

witnessed this myself, but no one is sure why it happens. Before taking things further, the larva may swing its abdomen from side to side to make sure that it is properly hooked on and to check for any obstacles in the vicinity, which could include other emerging Dragonflies. It may use its legs to check for obstacles, too. If something is in the way, the wings may not be able to expand properly, which could have disastrous consequences.

Off with the old

After an apparent rest, the breakout begins. By swallowing air, the larva raises its internal pressure and its exoskeleton cracks open on the back of the head and the thorax. The insect takes its time but gradually and with great effort pulls its head, thorax and legs, and a bit of abdomen, out of the old exoskeleton. The larva enters the 'resting stage', with part of its abdomen still inside its redundant skin. The rest of its body hangs down in some species, is upright in others and is horizontal in clubtails.

The hangers include demoiselles (Calopterygidae), hawkers (Aeshnidae), goldenrings (Cordulegastridae) and chasers, skimmers, darters and perchers (Libellulidae). The upright emergers include Emerald damselflies (Lestidae) and pond damselflies (Coenagrionidae).

The soft, emerging adult begins to harden up. The lull in activity comes to an end. The emerging adult repositions itself so that its legs

Right: A Club-tailed Dragonfly
Gomphus vulgatissimus
emerging (in sequence,
beginning from the top
image). This species will
emerge on horizontal and
vertical surfaces. It is even
known to have emerged on
someone's lawn!

can take hold of its old skin, and the
entire abdomen is pulled free of its old
life. But the insect is not its full size yet.
To achieve that, it must pump body
fluid (haemolymph) into its abdomen
and wings. The abdomen enlarges, the
crumpled wings expand and, bit-by-
bit, the adult takes shape. Observations
in Britain suggest that a damselfly can
emerge in an hour or two and one of the
bigger true dragonflies in two to four
hours. Some time later, the young adult
embarks on its first flight. On a good day
it could be on the wing in less than half
an hour after emergence, or within an
hour or two for the bigger Dragonflies.
Low temperatures or rain can slow things
down and have been known to postpone
a maiden flight for up to a week.

Emergence is a dangerous time. Aside
from getting the process itself right,
the not-yet-adult makes an easy meal
for a whole host of creatures including
slugs, spiders, Water Scorpions, fish,
frogs, newts, crocodiles, various birds,
Dragonflies, ants, hornets, cats and mice.

Freshly emerged Dragonflies are pale
and vulnerable. The survivors will fly
away from the water and, with time, take
on the colours of a mature adult. Then a
new chapter begins.

Opposite page, right:
The exuvia of a Southern
Hawker *Aeshna cyanea*
is discarded on a plant
stem after emergence. The
larval skin that an emerged
Dragonfly leaves behind is
known as its exuvia (the
plural is exuviae). Some are
easier to find than others,
but exuviae are irrefutable
proof that a species has
bred successfully. Seeing
Dragonflies mating or
egg-laying is a good sign,
but it doesn't guarantee that
a new generation will emerge.
Finding exuviae shows that
one has.

Resources

Books

General

Corbet, P. S., *A Biology of Dragonflies*, Classey, 1983.

Corbet, P. S. and S. Brooks, *Dragonflies*, Collins, 2008.

Corbet, P. S., *Dragonflies: Behaviour and Ecology of Odonata*, Harley Books, 1999.

Miller, P. L., *Dragonflies, Naturalists' Handbooks 7*, Richmond Publishing, 1995.

Nelson, B. and R. Thompson, *The Natural History of Ireland's Dragonflies*, The National Museums and Galleries of Northern Ireland, 2004.

Field Guides

Abbott, J. C., *Dragonflies and Damselflies of Texas and the South-Central United States*, Princeton, 2005.

Askew, R. R., *The Dragonflies of Europe*, Harley Books, 2004.

Brooks, S., and R. Lewington, *Field Guide to the Dragonflies and Damselflies of Great Britain and Ireland*, British Wildlife Publishing, 1999.

Cham, S., *Field Guide to the larvae and exuviae of British Dragonflies, Volume 1: Dragonflies (Anisoptera)*, The British Dragonfly Society, 2007.

Chinery, M., *Insects of Britain and Western Europe*, A&C Black, 2007.

Dijkstra, K-D. B. and R. Lewington *Field Guide to the Dragonflies of Britain and Europe*, British Wildlife Publishing, 2006.

Dunkle, S. W., *Guide to Dragonflies of Australia*, CSIRO Publishing, 2006.

Greenhalgh, M. and D. Ovenden, *Freshwater life, Britain and Northern Europe*, Collins, 2007.

Nikula, B., J. Sones and D. & L. Stokes, *Beginners Guide to Dragonflies*, Little, Brown and Company, 2002.

Samways, M. J., *Dragonflies and Damselflies of South Africa*, Pensoft, 2008.

Smallshire, D., and A. Swash, *Britain's Dragonflies*, Wildguides, 2004.

Theischinger, G. and J. Hawking, *The Complete Field Dragonflies through Binoculars, A Field Guide to Dragonflies of North America*, Oxford University Press, 2000.

Scientific papers

Allen, K. A. and D. J. Thompson, 'Movement characteristics of the Scarce Blue-tailed Damselfly, *Ischnura pumilio*', *Insect Conservation and Diversity*, Vol. 3, 2010, 5–14. Published online at onlinelibrary.wiley.com/doi/10.1111/j.1752-4598.2009.00070.x/abstract.

Anderson, R. C., 'Do dragonflies migrate across the western Indian Ocean?' *Journal of Tropical Ecology*, Vol. 25, 2009, 347–358.

Carle, F. L., 'A new *Epiophlebia* (Odonata: Epiophlebioidea) from China with a review of epiophlebian taxonomy, life history, and biogeography', *Arthropod Systematics & Phylogeny*, Vol. 70 (2), 75–83. Published online at www.arthropod-systematics.de on 28.ix.2012.

Catling, P. M. 'Dragonflies (Odonata) emerging from brackish pools in saltmarshes of Gaspé (Quebec), *Can.*

Fld. Nat., Vol. 123, 2009, 176–177.

Donoughe, S., J. D. Crall, R. A. Merz, and S. A. Combes, 'Resilin in dragonfly and damselfly wings and its implications for wing flexibility', *Journal of Morphology*, 2011. Published online at onlinelibrary.wiley.com and ebookbrowse. com/2011donoughecrallcombes-resilin-in-dragonfly-and-damselfly-wings-pdf-d385235428.

Ferreras-Romero, M., and P. S. Corbet, 'The life cycle of *Cordulegaster boltonii* (Donovan, 1807) (Odonata: Cordulegastridae) in the Sierra Morena mountains (southern Spain)', *Hydrobiologica*, Vol. 405, 1999, 39–48.

Harris, W., G. S. Parry, and D. W. Forman, 'Predation of Odonate larvae by Otters (*Lutra lutra*)', *J. Br. Dragonfly Society*, Vol. 23, No. 1, 2007.

Hobson, K. A., R. C. Anderson, D. X. Soto, and L. I. Wassenaar, 'Isotopic evidence that dragonflies (*Pantala flavescens*) migrating through the Maldives come from the northern Indian subcontinent', available at PLoS ONE 7(12): e52594. doi:10.1371/journal. pone.0052594.

Jödicke, R., J-P. Boudot, G. Jacquemin, B. Samraoui, and W. Schneider, 'Critical species of Odonata in northern Africa and the Arabian Peninsula', *International Journal of Odonatology*, Vol. 7, No. 2, 2004, 239–253.

Kalkman, V. J., V. Clausnitzer, K-D. B. Dijkstra, A. G. Orr, D. R. Paulson, and J. van Tol, 'Global diversity of dragonflies (Odonata) in freshwater', *Hydrobiologica* Vol. 595, 2008, 351–363. Published online at link.springer.com.

Kerbiriou, C., B. Bargain, I Le Viol, and S. Pavoine, 'Diet and fuelling of the globally threatened aquatic warbler at autumn migration stopover as compared with two congeners', *Anim. Conserv.* Vol. 14, Issue 3, 2011, 261–270. Also on onlinelibrary.wiley.com. First published online 30 November 2010.

Levett, S., and S. Walls, 'Tracking the elusive life of the Emperor Dragonfly *Anax imperator*', *J. Br. Dragonfly Society*, Vol. 27, No. 1, 2011.

Petrin, Z., E. G. Schilling, C. S. Loftin, and F. Johansson, 'Predators shape distribution and promote diversification of morphological defenses in *Leucorrhinia*', *Odonata Evol. Ecol.*, Vol. 24, 2010, 1003–1016.

Weihrauch, F., 'A review of the distribution of Odonata in the Macaronnesian Islands, with particular reference to the *Ischnura* puzzle', *J. Br. Dragonfly Society*, Vol. 27, No. 1, 2011.

Wikelski, M., D. Moskowitz, J. S. Adelman, J. Cochran, D. S. Wilcove, and M. L. May, 'Simple rules guide dragonfly migration', *Biol. Lett.*, vol. 2, no. 3, 2006, 325–329. Published online at http://rsbl.royalsocietypublishing.org/content/2/3/ - aff-5.

Websites

Africa Dragonfly: www.africa-dragonfly.net
Birding Hawaii: www.birdinghawaii.co.uk
British Dragonfly Society: www.british-dragonflies.org.uk
Charles Anderson discovers dragonflies that cross oceans: www.ted.com/talks/charles_anderson_discovers_dragonflies_that_cross_oceans.html
Dragonflies and damselflies of Ecuador: bdei2.cs.umb.

edu/~whaber/Odonata_of_Ecuador/index.html

Dragonflies of Manitoba: www.naturenorth.com/dragonfly/DOM

Dragonfly sizes: mailweb.pugetsound.edu/pipermail/odonata-l/2006-January/005943.html

Epiophlebia laidlaiwi in IUCN red list: www.iucnredlist.org/details/7896/0

Epiophlebia superstes in Odonata on stamps: defworld.freeoda.com/Species%20Details/Epiophlebia%20superstes.html

Integrated Taxonomic Information System: www.itis.gov

Minnesota Odonata Survey Project: www.mndragonfly.org

Nehalennia speciosa: www.arkive.org/dwarf-damselfly/nehalennia-speciosa

NW dragonflier blogspot: nwdragonflier.blogspot.co.uk/2011/02/zenithoptera-morpho-of-dragonflies.html

The Papua Insects Foundation: www.papua-insects.nl

Reserva Ecológica de Guapiaçu: www.regua.co.uk

South African National Biodiversity Institute: www.sanbi.org

Vagrant Emperor *Anax ephippiger* in Cornwall, England, 2011: www.cornishnature.co.uk/cornish-dragonflies/57-the-vagrant-emperor-anax-ephippiger-.html

What bug is that? The guide to Australian insect families: anic.ento.csiro.au/insectfamilies

Also available in this series:

Barn Owl by David Chandler.
£12.99 ISBN 978 1 84773 768 7

Kingfisher by Ian Llewellyn and David Chandler.
£12.99 ISBN 978 1 84773 524 9

Peregrine Falcon by Patrick Sterling-Aird.
£12.99 ISBN 978 1 84773 769 4

Other Insect Books by New Holland Publishers include:

Concise Insect Guide
£4.99 ISBN 978 1 84773 604 8

Concise Pond Wildlife Guide
£4.99 ISBN 978 1 84773 9773

Concise Butterfly & Moth Guide
£4.99 ISBN 978 1 84773 602 4

Steve Backshall's Deadly 60
£9.99 ISBN 978 1 84773 430 3

Nick Baker's Bug Book
£9.99 ISBN 978 1 84773 522 5

Colouring Bugs by Sally MacLarty
£2.99 ISBN 978 1 84773 525 6

All About... Bugs! by David Chandler
£4.99 ISBN 978 1 84773 051 0

Creative Nature Photography by Bill Coster
£19.99 ISBN 978 1 84773 784 7

PAPILIO

FOCUS DOWN TO 50cm – YOU CAN'T GET ANY CLOSER THAN THIS

- CLOSE Technology allows close focus to 50 cm – absolutely unique!
- BaK4 prism and multi-coated lenses for enhanced light transmission and resolution
- Dual-axis, 290 g, single body housing with synchronized IPD adjustment
- Aspherical lens elements to assure edge-to-edge sharpness
- Inner focusing so dust cannot disrupt functionality – low maintenance means long life
- Two models with 6.5 or 8.5x magnification for variable field-of-view

www.pentax.co.uk

Index